Don't Give Up On Me!

Supporting Aging Parents Successfully

A DAUGHTER'S INTIMATE MEMOIR

By Jan Simpson

CIRCLE
OF LIFE
PARTNERS

The aging journey can be challenging...
let us be your guide.™
978-287-5600 www.colpartners.com

With gratitude

for the wit, wisdom, and grace

of my parents

Contents

The Last Years

Foreword

MY MOTHER WAS FORGETFUL. My father had cancer. They called me for help and asked their lawyer to draw up some papers. I'd like to say that I thought carefully about my decision to offer support and that I fully understood what this decision would entail, but in truth, I was clueless.

Their solicitation of my help was not altogether unexpected. Although I have four siblings, I am the youngest daughter, and so it seemed only natural for me to bear most of the responsibility for their well-being as they grew older. At the time, my children were three and six years old, I was working part-time as a business consultant, and I lived in a town neighboring my parents. I had been helping them a bit already, providing homemade soups and casseroles, and occasionally driving them to doctor appointments. I guess I expected these duties to continue with a few new tasks, such as paying their bills, added to my responsibilities. Their request seemed reasonable since we had always had a close relationship.

My parents were members of what historians have called the greatest generation. Born in 1919 and 1920, they witnessed the widespread unemployment and disruption caused by the Great Depression. They married in 1940. Although exempt from military service, my father had enlisted in the Navy during World War II. Following the war, they did what many of their generation did: they raised their children, were good neighbors, and were active members of their church.

As their youngest child, I saw nothing remarkable in them. They never talked about the war; they didn't value material possessions; they didn't want to travel or write books or solve society's ills. They were not dreamers. They seemed content to live out their lives quietly, simply grateful that unlike so many of their generation, they were able to do so. Through their fifties and sixties, medical issues arose like small waves on the beach, but caused only minimal disruption in their lives. They enjoyed their children and grandchildren and friends. As they entered their seventies, however, their medical issues became more severe, creating galelike storms which rallied our family to their aid, until the winds subsided and calm was restored. They met each crisis as they had lived—with good humor, strength, and grace. "Old age isn't for wimps," my father often joked, "but it sure beats the alternative!"

The last chapter in their lives began with a telephone call from their doctor: an x-ray had shown that my father had lung cancer. One telephone call to schedule surgery and another call to their lawyer set in motion the events described in this book. I signed the legal documents without thought, expecting to be involved for a couple of years, until the dust settled and life returned to normal. Six years later, I began to write their story.

Don't Give Up on Me! documents my journey with my parents over a decade as I struggled to manage their care while raising my own family and keeping my sanity. I wrote the book as I lived the experience, though I have altered the names of some characters to preserve their anonymity. Within these pages, you'll meet my parents and their doctors—some capable, some not. You'll meet my siblings and friends—some helpful, some not. You'll discover a medical system filled with neglect, incompetence, skill, and compassion. You'll understand the legal aspects of elder care and learn how we used their modest financial resources to keep them at home until they died. Above all, you'll see how we coped as a family with the escalating demands of the dying and how we found countless ways to enjoy our last years with them.

This book is about supporting aging parents and about the gift those parents bring to our adult lives. Like parenting children, there are no clear-cut answers, no forewarnings of crises pending, no clear road maps to follow. Each family situation is different. The decisions we made were often done with limited information, under time pressure, or in response to the stresses and strains of caregiving. We made mistakes. We found resources. We learned from each other. We did the best we could.

I wrote this book to help those of you who find yourselves worrying about your parents as they enter the last chapter of their lives. I want you to understand some of the choices that have to be made and to encourage you to journey those last miles alongside your parents: stay your course. Just as children, regardless of whether they are parented well, will grow into adults, your parents, regardless of whether you intervene, will continue to age and one day succumb to their illnesses. The quality of their life, however, their ability to enjoy life near its end, may depend on you. I hope that you can learn from our experience and create a web of support for your parents. What you don't know, what you don't do, may end their lives prematurely. It is worth the effort.

The events described in the book are gleaned from a number of sources: medical records, their medical diaries, e-mails, letters, conversations, and a personal journal. All events are described from my perspective, a perspective that occasionally was blurred from exhaustion, grief, and anger. I accept that others may describe events differently. By altering the names of the characters, I have felt freer to write with candor, particularly about our family dynamics. I love my siblings dearly, but, at times, their behavior, and probably mine, was maddening. That, too, is part of the story.

This book began to take shape six years after that initial telephone call. I never intended to write a book; I had only hoped to help my parents live well through their last years. But as friends began to experience changes in their parents' lives, I realized that perhaps I should share our experience. When I mentioned the book to my husband, his only advice was, "You'd better make it funny. No one wants to know the truth."

So here it is, funny, sad, disturbing, outrageous, but also the truth. Be prepared to laugh, to cry, to scream, and also to marvel at the resilience of my parents. It is an honor to be their daughter.

The Start of the Journey

ONE / Crisis

T HE TELEPHONE RANG as I shut down the computer in my home office. I hesitated, debating whether to answer or let the machine pick up the call. In a few minutes I had to retrieve my daughter from school. She was five years old, in kindergarten, and her school day ended at noon. It was 11:15. I answered the phone.

"Jan, I'm in trouble," he croaked into the receiver.

"What do you mean by trouble?" I replied. I didn't need to ask who was calling.

"I can't breathe." His words rushed out. "I tried calling Dr. Harmon, but he's on vacation. I can call the police or get an ambulance, but they'll take me to the Lahey Clinic. I don't know what to do."

I was worried. My father never panicked. For eight years he had raced cancer and repeatedly beat the odds: when throat cancer weakened his voice and threatened his life, he burned the vocal cords into remission with radiation; when arteries clogged with plaque threatened his heart, he joked about new plumbing and bypassed those blockages with veins from his legs; when a slight pain in his chest turned out to be lung cancer, he cajoled the hospital bureaucracy into removing the diseased lung. Within months he was driving his car and climbing stairs. Strong, willful, a survivor. The master dueling with death.

"The secret to longevity," he once boasted, "is to stay on top of each medical crisis. You can't ignore the signs." He paused; his comedic timing was impeccable. "That," he joked, "and choosing your parents wisely."

His quiet voice now shrieked with anguish.

"No, you don't want to go to Lahey," I said forcing control into my

3

voice. "They have all of your records at Mount Auburn Hospital." *You'll have a better chance there,* I didn't add.

"I'll be right over to drive you," I said. "Get ready."

I hung up the receiver and leaned against the wall. Eyes closed, my stomach sank. I felt numb. A sudden thought flashed into my head. I redialed his number.

"Hello?" he whispered.

"Dad, where's Mom?" I asked brusquely.

"She's upstairs doing something," he replied, a hint of impatience in his voice.

"Put her on please," I demanded.

A pause. A moment later I heard him call out weakly, "Muriel? Muriel? Pick up the telephone. Jan wants to talk to you." I waited tapping my foot on the floor.

"Hello?"

"Mom," I called, my voice tense and sharp, "I need you to do something for me."

"Oh, Jan," she said, oblivious to my urgency. "How are you?"

"Mom," I repeated, raising my voice as though it would help, "Dad is in trouble. I'm coming over to take him to the hospital. Do you understand me? I'm coming over. I need you to pack his blue suitcase with some clothes. He will probably stay overnight in the hospital. Okay? Mom? Okay? Do you understand? You need to pack his suitcase."

"Okay," she said cheerfully.

"I'll be right over," I snapped, hanging up the telephone. I knew that even if she didn't find his clothes, my assignment would keep her away from him. My thoughts began to race, accelerating to warp speed.

Okay, now what? Think, Jan. Think. I quickly dialed a friend's number. *Oh please, God,* I prayed. *Have Barb be there...be there...be there.*

"Hello?" Barb's voice echoed on the line.

"Oh, Barb, my father is very ill. Could you pick up Katie from school today?"

"Of course," she said.

I cut her off. "I have to rush him to the hospital."

"And what about Eric?" she inquired about my son. "Why don't I get him at 3:30? That way you don't have to rush back."

"Thanks," I said hurriedly, "I'll call the school."

I felt flush. I began to run through the house. I found my shoes. I grabbed my jacket. I carried the portable telephone to make one last call. I punched in the numbers.

"Country Day School, Helen Flint speaking." A smooth, unruffled tone, no doubt a calming sound for harried parents. Not today.

"Helen," I snapped. "This is Jan Simpson. My father is seriously ill and I need to rush him to the hospital." The words spit out like venom. "Barb Summers will be taking both of my kids home with her today. Could you please tell their teachers?"

"Oh," she replied laconically. "We can't release any children without a note." Her words curled around my ears like the tongue of a hissing snake.

A note? A note? I wanted to reach through the telephone and grab her collar.

"Helen," I continued in disbelief, "This-is-an-emergency. My father is very ill."

"I'm sorry," she responded. "We can't release any children without a signed note."

"Okay," I interrupted. I quickly calculated the time to deliver a note to the school. It would take too long. *Think, Jan, think.*

Fax!

"Helen," I said, trying to keep the anger out of my voice, "Do you have a fax machine?"

"Yes," she replied quizzically.

"May I fax a note to you?" I asked.

"Well," she replied, stretching out each letter as if yawning, "I don't know. We like to have notes ..."

"Please, Helen," I interrupted, pleading. "Please! I need to get to my father!"

"Okay," she replied, reluctantly giving me the school's fax number.

I ran into my home office for paper. I shouted out the words as I rapidly wrote them down, "Barbara-Summers-has-my-permission-to-take-my-children-Katie-and-Eric-home-today-at-dismissal."

I scribbled my signature and raced up the stairs to the fax machine. I entered the school number and marched in place as the paper slowly slid into the machine. My hands held my head in anguish as I cried aloud in the empty room: "My father is going to die, and I have to send you this damn note!"

"Hurry, hurry!" I shouted when the lines connected.

I was halfway down the flight of stairs when I heard the horn signal that the fax had gone through successfully. I flew out the door and jumped into my car. I raced through the streets of Concord, Bedford, and Lexington to Woburn. I had driven these roads hundreds of times over the past five years. I followed the back streets, taking shortcuts, avoiding lights, and ignoring stop signs on the empty roads. Minutes might matter, I kept thinking.

Before long, I was on my parents' doorstep. I banged on the back door. My father opened it. Dressed in an undershirt and slacks, he panted heavily as I helped him get into his dress shirt. I spied his blue suitcase near a living room chair.

"Mom," I called up the stairs.

"Yes," she sang pleasantly.

"Come down, now. We have to take Dad to the hospital."

I found my father's jacket and helped him into it.

"Mom," I called again. "We're getting into the car...now!"

I walked my father to the car and buckled him into his seat belt. He held a small towel in his hand and his breath came in quick pants.

"Where is she?" I asked impatiently as I closed the passenger door of the car. I raced into the house and grabbed the suitcase.

"Mom, if you don't come down now, I have to leave you here!" I barked. "Dad must get to the hospital!"

Within a minute, she followed me out of the house and climbed into the backseat. I pulled quickly out of the driveway.

On a typical day, the drive to the hospital might have taken twenty-five minutes. My mother made light conversation from the backseat, seemingly unaware of the crisis at hand. I interrupted her chatter to talk to my dad, who seemed to be struggling mightily to stay conscious. He held the towel near his face.

"Dad," I said. "Do you feel like you're going to be sick?"

"No," he whispered. "Just drive."

I drove with both feet, trying to minimize the hesitation at stop signs and red lights. I grabbed my cell phone and called Dr. Harmon's office.

"Sandy," I said to his nurse. "This is Jan Simpson, Bob Albertson's daughter. I'm bringing my father to the emergency room. He's having trouble breathing."

"I know," she said. "I talked with him this morning."

"Good," I replied. "I know that Dr. Harmon is away. Who's on call for him?"

"Dr. Feingold."

"Good," I said hurriedly, watching my dad out of the corner of my eye. "Could you contact him and tell him that my dad is going to be there in about fifteen minutes?"

"No," she replied. "The emergency room will do that when he gets there."

"Okay," I responded, feeling my face flush with annoyance. "Then could you call the E.R. and tell them to expect him so they can take him immediately?"

"No," she hesitated. "It's not our policy..."

I did not want to hear the rest of her explanation. I felt like screaming at her, but I remained calm. If my dad weren't so ill, I might have told her what I really thought about that policy. That would only have upset him though, and he was having enough trouble already.

"Okay," I said and hung up.

"They'll take you as soon as you get there," I lied.

"Good," he replied, with his eyes focused on the road ahead.

To any passengers in neighboring cars, I might have looked like the dutiful daughter taking her elderly parents out for a morning ride. The shared panic between my father and me led to silence. While I concentrated on driving, he concentrated on breathing.

"Go!" he whispered urgently once, when I didn't jump at a green light.

In the silence, voices screamed in my head. *This is so stupid, Jan.*

What are you doing? What will you do if he stops breathing? You'll be stuck on the highway with a demented woman and a dying old man!

Shut up! I forced myself to focus on my driving.

I whipped into the emergency entrance at the hospital and pulled into an open parking space. My dad crawled out of the car before it came to a full stop, his mouth covered with the towel. He shuffled quickly toward the automatic door. My mother sat in the backseat.

"Go with him, Mom," I prompted. "I'll park the car and come right back." She followed my father through the hospital door.

I pulled quickly out of the emergency driveway but not before glancing in my rearview mirror to be sure that he got into the building safely.

I drove up the ramp to the parking garage, grabbed the ticket, swept down two levels, and parked. I leapt out of the car, bounded up two flights of stairs, flew across the front lawn of the hospital and around the side toward the emergency entrance. I paused for a second at the entrance as the door opened for me and then I rushed into the emergency room. No one was at the desk. I looked beyond the desk through the window in the triage room and saw my dad surrounded by nurses. "Thank God," I sighed, shutting my eyes and taking a deep breath to calm down.

Suddenly, my mind snapped to attention. *Where's Mom?*

I quickly scanned the emergency room. It was empty. I turned back toward the entrance, where a security guard was stationed. As I approached the door, I spied my mother seated in a chair pressed against the wall, and I walked toward her. Her face was placid, her hands folded neatly on her lap.

"Oh, Mom," I said with relief. "I see that they have Dad."

"Yes," she smiled. A long silence followed. "He decided to get a flu shot before we went upstairs."

"A flu shot?" I turned quizzically toward the nurses' station.

A flu shot? What the hell is he doing getting a flu shot now? I felt another adrenaline surge and stomped over toward the nurses' station.

Halfway there, I stopped. A flu shot? I looked at my father through the treatment window; I looked at my mother, waiting patiently near the door. The realization came like a gust of wind. I was stunned. For years, I had puzzled endlessly about her. Now, suddenly, I understood. Like the solution to a complex brainteaser, the answer was obvious, simple and unexpected. It took just three words.

"Oh good," I nodded as I walked back toward her and slumped into a chair. "A flu shot."

My father was admitted to the hospital. Ten days later, he was discharged and sent home into my mother's care. That night, he called 911. He was taken by ambulance to a local community hospital where he died.

TWO / Family History

MY PARENTS MET IN 1936, when my mother was just sixteen years old. A dark-haired beauty, smart, slim, well dressed, and well mannered, her appearance and demeanor belied the fact that she was raised with three siblings in an eight-family tenement in Cambridge, Massachusetts. During the Great Depression, her father struggled to find work while one of her older brothers left home to work on public works projects with the Works Progress Administration. Her lingering memory from those years was of a pot of soup simmering on the stove, which her mother provided to anyone in the neighborhood who needed a warm meal.

My father was the youngest son of an Irish immigrant who, by intellect and effort, rose through the ranks to become the owner and general manager of a small textile mill in Boston. Raised in Andover, Massachusetts, just blocks away from Phillips Academy, my father's family was unaffected by the ravages of the Depression. As a boy, he worked as a groom in stables near the academy where he met many well-heeled locals. Blond-haired and blue-eyed, it was no surprise that my father won my mother with his handsome appearance and the casual confidence prescribed by his relative affluence.

Following high school, my father, like his father before him, found employment in a textile mill where he learned a trade and became a master machinist. In 1940, he married my mother; my siblings Bill and Carol were born before he enlisted in the Navy during World War II. After the war, my father found employment at the Boston Naval Shipyard, which offered secure work repairing naval ships, good benefits, and a government pension. Although eligible for GI educational benefits from his service during the war, he had no time to obtain a college education, for he spent his evenings working the second job needed to cover the bills from his growing family. My mother had dropped out of high school her senior year to recover from a broken leg. She never returned.

Like many women of her day, my mother devoted her time and energy to raising her family. My oldest siblings, Bill, Carol, and Walter, were born in the 1940s. My sister Ginny and I were born more than a decade later, creating almost two distinct families. My older siblings were influenced by Elvis, the Beatles, and the Vietnam War; Ginny and I were daughters of the seventies.

Church, education, and family were the core values of my parents' lives. While my father worked, my mother managed the house, five children, and what little money we had. By shopping wisely, in thrift stores, mills, and outlets, she set aside pennies and quarters for our education. She made our clothes, crocheted afghans, and stretched meals to feed her hungry brood. The fact that the five of us share twelve college and graduate degrees is a testament to my parents' efforts and to my mother's skills in money management.

My early childhood was typical of life reflected in the then popular television shows *Leave It to Beaver* and *Father Knows Best*. We lived in a large Irish Catholic neighborhood where I was never at a loss for playmates. We built forts, climbed trees, and played games like kickball in the street. We skated on the neighborhood pond in winter, swam in our above-ground pools in summer, sold lemonade, and organized backyard fairs. Although most families had little money to spare, we had all that we needed: sunshine, good friends, and a solid bicycle.

My relationship with my parents was shaped largely by my position in the family. As the youngest child, I received all the benefits of having experienced parents and few of the hassles. In fact, my oldest three siblings would say that Ginny and I had it easy because they had worn down my father and dampened his Irish temperament. They had indeed. Along the way, he had learned to parent differently, imparting advice through humorous storytelling instead of commanding directives. As the youngest of four boys, my father had a natural understanding of my place in the family.

"For years, I thought my name was Bobby Do," he joked, making light of the ease with which the others would use him as their runner. "You know, as in 'Bobby, do this...and Bobby, do that.'"

"My mother always wanted one gentleman in the family," he continued, retelling a familiar tale as we lingered over Sunday dinner. "By the time I reached school age, she had given up on my three older brothers who were hellions. So, I was going to be it. When I was nine or ten, she made me go to dance classes. Can you imagine that? Next to forcing an active boy to wash with soap and water, I can't think of anything worse than forcing a ten-year-old boy to learn how to dance." He paused, shaking his head.

"My dancing partner was the fat daughter of one of my mother's best friends. She and her friends constantly teased me in school about dance class. It was hell. I knew I couldn't punch her though, my mother would kill me."

"One day, though," he said, eyes twinkling, "I got even. I walked by her table during lunch and slipped a worm into her milk carton." He grinned mischievously. "She took a few sips before she noticed the worm. When she did, she started screaming. And when her friends sitting nearby saw the worm, they started screaming too." Even decades later, the story filled him with such amusement that his hearty laugh interrupted his telling. "But that wasn't all," he continued when his laughter subsided. "She got so worked up she started to vomit. And her friends followed suit, one after the other, like the wave you'll see fans make at Fenway Park. It was amazing!"

"Bob," my mother chided, "Do you have to tell this story while we're eating?" Like George Burns and Gracie Allen, my mother often played the foil for his jokes and stories. He was the Irish raconteur and she, the prim English lady.

By now, we were all convulsing with laughter.

"Boy," he continued, ignoring my mother, "did I get into trouble, first in school and later when I got home. But you know what?" He paused, with perfect timing. He had our rapt attention. "It was worth it. My mother finally let me drop the dance classes."

When we were young, my father's stories focused on the silly antics of unbridled boys in a small New England town. As we grew older, the stories changed to include the wilder behavior of adolescent males. Looking back, I can see that his stories had common themes: be responsible, think independently, stand up for yourself, be accountable for your actions, no slackers. As a child, I absorbed these messages unwittingly, incorporating a fierce, independent spirit into my tomboyish behavior. Unlike other girls, who were encouraged to take up ballet or baton twirling, I was expected to hold my own in the rough-and-tumble nature of our neighborhood. My mother, no doubt, was appalled by a telephone call reporting that I had smacked a neighborhood bully on the head with a broomstick as he wrestled my sister to the ground, but my father—he had to leave the room to hide his amusement. He later joked with my brother Walter, "Pity the poor bastard who tries to steal a kiss from her!"

I adored my father and, as a child, I developed strong feelings of attachment to my mother, not from typical mother-daughter connections, but rather from something quite different: I felt that I needed to protect her.

I was too young to remember the year my grandparents and aunt died, but I lived with the aftermath. One summer, my father's mother passed away from complications of lung cancer, acquired from secondhand smoke. Three months later, my grandfather, driving home from the cemetery he visited daily, pulled over to the side of the road and died. The death certificate said "sudden death—natural causes, cerebral thrombosis," but the family knew he died of a broken heart. The intensity of losing both parents and the size of my grandfather's estate led to a legal battle over the distribution of assets. In the end, instead of inheriting tens of thousands of dollars each, money that would have helped my parents pay off their mortgage or pay college tuition, each son inherited only a few thousand dollars; court costs and legal bills devoured the rest. I can only imagine the stress on my mother, whose gentle manner was drowned by the volatility of a contentious family battle, so destructive that one of my uncles left the area, never to see or speak to my father again. As if that were not enough turmoil, six months later, my mother's sister died. She had elective back surgery to correct a disc problem and died in the recovery room, leaving three young children to the fates and an alcoholic father. My parents tried to intervene, but they were blocked from having ongoing contact with the children. Distress over the loss of her young sister and concern for her nieces and nephew only compounded my mother's grief.

Then, her mother died. I was seven, and when I arrived home from school one fall afternoon, my father told me that my grandmother had passed away from complications of diabetes. I found my mother lying in her bed, alone in her darkened room, brilliant sun shining through the edges of the drawn shades. She was not asleep, but she did not want to talk to me. I was frightened for her, and Ginny must have felt the same. I still retain a vivid memory of us playing silently with our Barbie dolls on the floor beside my mother's bed, two sentinels guarding our mother who seemed so vulnerable and in need of our protection.

For many years, my mother hid the devastation she felt after the loss of her mother and sister. Although lingering grief caused migraine headaches that sometimes forced her to the couch, she remained gentle with us, never raising her voice, forever placating the intense, independent spirits of her children, organizing quiet celebrations of our successes, buffeting us from the vagaries of the world. Her sadness surfaced only briefly around the holidays and in the spring.

Perhaps our awareness of her hidden vulnerability explains the career paths Ginny and I chose. Ginny became an educator, working with children and adults with disabilities. She has spent her entire career in an inner city, coordinating support services for thousands of children while raising her own four children and completing a doctorate so she could teach others how to do the same.

I went along a different career path, intending to become a minister or a physician. Shortly before an acceptance letter from Tufts University arrived, however, I learned that my father was being forced to take an early retirement. Tuition would be expensive, well beyond what I had saved, and I quickly applied to the University of Massachusetts Lowell, never telling my parents the true reason for the sudden change in my decision. Both of my brothers had graduated from Lowell and had attended graduate schools elsewhere. They had fared well, I reasoned, and I would do the same, saving my parents' money. Although my passions were history and languages, I majored in chemistry, hoping that by achieving good grades in a rigorous major I might still have the opportunity to attend medical school. My parents never questioned my decision. They were very pleased when I graduated from Lowell and went to work full-time for an aerospace company to save money for my next degree.

My mother's psychiatric troubles exploded the winter following my college graduation as I made plans to move into an apartment with two friends. That February, she seemed withdrawn, sleeping often; she remained in bed, distant and glassy-eyed, for hours, talking with God. My father called the minister for guidance. My brothers and sisters came to see her. There was much discussion about what to do. One Saturday morning, her behavior worsened. She and I were standing near the top of the stairwell, and as I turned to go downstairs, she gave me a shove to hurry. I lost my footing, and for a few seconds was suspended above the staircase, grasping wildly for the railing and for a way to break my fall. That day she was brought to Newton-Wellesley Hospital and admitted to the psychiatric unit.

During one visit, I sat with her in the patient dayroom as she stared eerily up at the ceiling, begging me to take her home. I was horrified. I was told later that the staring was a side effect of Thorazine, the drug given to calm her down. Apparently, it didn't work, for a few days later I was told that she was going to be moved to Charles River Hospital, a private psychiatric hospital, because she was an escape risk. In the psychiatric unit at Newton-Wellesley Hospital, she was a patient of her own volition. She could sign herself out, even against doctor's orders. At Charles River, however, she could be committed against her wishes and held more safely behind locked doors.

I was uneasy after the transfer, and I scheduled a visit with her alone. I drove through Wellesley center, past upscale boutiques and shops, and turned left down a side street off the center of town. I was dreading my visit, fully expecting to find her raging in a decrepit brick building with barred windows, like many of the state mental institutions dotting the highways. I was shocked to pull into the driveway of what appeared to be a mansion. More shocking was my mother's mental state. She greeted me cheerfully and sat chatting in a lunchroom. She was her old self again.

When she had arrived at Charles River Hospital, they took her off all medication to see how she would behave. Surprisingly, she behaved normally. When the hospital asked why she was there, she said, "Because my family thinks I'm crazy." We took her home the next day and put the episode behind us. Her psychosis was attributed to an allergic reaction to the medication erythromycin. This diagnosis would prove incorrect.

Four years later, I observed that my father seemed sleep deprived and exhausted. I discovered that my mother had been staying awake at night, all night, and was keeping my father up too, so I offered to sleep at their house while he went to Ginny's home in a neighboring town for a good night's rest. My mother and I, alone, retired around ten o'clock, but a few hours later I heard her roaming around the house. I got up and suggested that we have a pajama party and that she sleep in my room so we could talk for a while. She readily agreed, and for hours we stayed awake; she chatted nonstop, revealing many family secrets. How much of it all was true or imagined, I still don't know. After a few hours of chatting, her voice changed tone.

"You were always such a good girl," she sneered from the right side of the bed. Although I was able to doze through most of her chatter, my instincts suddenly awoke. Without warning, my mother grabbed the front of my nightgown and twisted it tightly around my neck. A slim 5'7" and more than twice my age, I knew my mother could not hurt me, but I was surprised by her physical strength. Horrified, I grabbed each of her wrists and using all of my body weight, I pushed my mother away from me, pinning her arms down to the bed. I held her down until she stopped resisting. Physically and mentally exhausted, she eventually drifted off to sleep. I sat up next to her for the rest of the night.

Early the next morning, I told Ginny about the incident and said that my mother had to go to a hospital. She could not be left alone with my father. Ginny found my mother a bed in the psychiatric unit of a local community hospital, Melrose-Wakefield. After two weeks of care, my mother returned home and slowly resumed her routines.

At the time, I was in my midtwenties, and had accomplished what my parents had hoped for each of their children. I held a good job, lived in an apartment with friends, and was able to support myself financially. I had recently completed a master's degree in chemistry, paid for by the company. I wasn't quite finished with my education, though.

"I'm going to Harvard," I told my parents one night over dinner at their house. "Truthfully, though, I am still in shock that they admitted me to the business school."

"Why?" my mother replied, passing the mashed potatoes to me.

"Well, no offense, Mom," I said laughing, "but we're not exactly the Rockefellers and it's not like I went to MIT or Yale. All I did was fill out the application and send it in. It's really shocking that they would admit someone like me."

"Are you set?" my father asked.

"I have enough money saved to cover the first year and keep my apartment," I said. "I'm not sure yet about the second year. For some reason, they don't want students to work during the academic year."

I couldn't imagine the luxury of simply taking classes and studying: since I was fourteen, I had always worked summers, weeknights, and weekends. After college, my hours reversed, working full-time, going to school in the evenings, and teaching chemistry to university students on the side.

A few days before classes at Harvard started, I stopped by my parents' house for tea. Sensing my anxiety, my father was full of stories. "So," he said, "you're going to be a Harvard man."

"Yeah," I replied grinning nervously, "I figure that I can't marry one, so I might as well become one!" He laughed and continued to regale me with stories about people he knew in Andover. As I packed up to leave, he wished me luck and smiled mischievously.

"Just remember, Jan, you can always tell a Harvard man, but you can't tell him much!"

How true.

THREE / Return to Boston

WITHIN TWO YEARS OF GRADUATING from business school, I was married and working in a global management position for Bristol-Myers Squibb, a pharmaceutical company with headquarters in Princeton, New Jersey. My husband Ron was with McKinsey & Company, a prestigious consulting firm that provides business advice to CEOs and senior executives in Fortune 100 companies. Smart, aggressive, and unpretentious, Ron's family story mirrored my own. Raised in a three-family home in Queens, New York, he was valedictorian at his high school, attended Manhattan College on a full scholarship, and acquired a master's degree in engineering from Princeton University. At Harvard Business School he graduated as a Baker Scholar, and he quickly became one of McKinsey's top consultants.

We were what people then called "dinks" (double income no kids) with soaring careers and few responsibilities. Yet we didn't quite fit the mold. Unlike our peers, who channeled their growing wallets into expensive cars, country club memberships, and large homes, we lived modestly in a two-bedroom townhouse, spending weekends and vacations with friends and family.

The pending birth of our first child brought some unanticipated changes in our lives. Shortly before our son was born, McKinsey assigned Ron to a client in northern California. Not wanting to miss out on the first year of his son's life, he approached the assignment director and requested an East Coast placement, explaining that this was his first child and that he wanted to be around to raise him.

"We all have families," was the cool response from his director, who subsequently left his wife and family to take up with his personal assistant. The firm offered to fly Ron home every week midweek if he insisted on seeing his son more often.

Displeased by their response, Ron left McKinsey and accepted an offer from an investment firm in New York City. After our son was born I returned to work, but the difficulty of finding dependable childcare, the knowledge that I had a backlog of international travel, and the tug of war between work and home forced me to rethink my priorities. I left Bristol-Myers Squibb that September and launched an independent consulting practice, networking with a dozen former executives caught up in the wave of downsizings and early retirements. Together we bid on assignments, working from home offices and small executive suites. The work was stimulating, and the flexibility gave me more time with our son.

Between assignments, I spent many afternoons at local parks, playing ball and scaling climbers. During that time, I began to reflect upon the direction our lives were taking us and the family life we were creating for our son Eric and his sister, whom I was carrying. If we stayed in Manhattan, the children would have everything in a material sense, but they would never have the simplicity of my own and Ron's childhoods. Despite our modest beginnings, we were raised in the loving stability of a large extended family, surrounded by grandparents, cousins, generous neighbors, and friends. By contrast, our children's lives would include nannies, country clubs, and preoccupied parents pressured by the all-consuming demands of work and social obligations.

Most disturbing was the growing realization that the expectation for the wife in my world was one of social hostess and well-dressed companion. Although some women led professional lives, most did not sustain them, needing to attend and plan countless dinners and benefits. Not surprising, divorce was routine and trophy wives were commonplace.

Unwittingly, motherhood had changed my worldview. It was evident that in this community, where people focus on the acquisition of money and power, family life takes a distant third place. If some of the McKinsey partners were somewhat insensitive to men who value their family time, the partners at his new employer seemed completely indifferent, one going so far as to rent an apartment under his penthouse suite where his infant daughter and nanny could live so the baby wouldn't disrupt his life. Instead of finding this world fascinating, like Lil' Orphan Annie in the world of Daddy Warbucks, I found the people to be narcissistic and their material wealth obscene.

"We're moving back to Boston," I told my father one afternoon, sitting in his living room while Eric napped upstairs.

"Oh? What about your work?"

"It doesn't matter," I replied. "I'm working as a consultant now, so I can live anywhere. I figure I'll run down to New York or New Jersey a few times a month, pick up work, and do it up here. With computers, faxes, and telephones, I can work from anywhere."

He seemed skeptical.

"Really, Dad," I continued. "It's easy these days to work from home, I've been doing it for two years now. I can work from Princeton or Boston. In fact, it will be easier from Boston. Right now, I'm alone most weekdays trying to work and raise Eric. It's ridiculous. In Boston, he'll be surrounded by family, aunts, uncles, and cousins. He won't feel so alone. Heck, I won't feel so alone."

"What about Ron?" he probed.

"For a while, Ron will work in New York. When the time is right, he'll look for another job. We both know that it is better for us to raise our children near family."

We sat in silence as I shifted my gaze from his face to the window and absently ran my fingers through my blond hair. Sensing the strain of this decision, his eyes caught mine and his face softened with understanding.

"Well, Jan," he said quietly, "remember, you can never go home again."

I paused to think about what this meant, willing away the tears that filled my eyes.

"I am not trying to go home, Dad," I sighed. "I am trying to put some distance between the kids and our lifestyle. I want them to have roots. I want them to live near family. I want them to be..." I hesitated, searching for the right word, "normal."

We sat again in silence.

"You know," he said, breaking the mood with a lilt in his voice. "My mother never went back to Ireland." I was grateful for the change in subject.

"Why not? Was the trip too expensive?"

"No, my father went back a few times, to Germany too, to see his brother Sam. But she wouldn't go back. She said that if she went back to Ireland, she'd never return to the States. You see, she was the oldest of thirteen children and her family was dirt poor. It would have been too hard for her to go back and see all of that."

"Yeah," I agreed. "I understand. It is difficult for anyone to live in two worlds."

I smiled with appreciation as we continued our conversation. As always, he did not tell me what to do; as always, his gentle probing kept me talking, weighing out the different parts of a decision until I became increasingly aware of what I was doing and why. He wanted me to be certain that I understood the risks.

The move would jeopardize our careers, which were still works in progress. The move could jeopardize our marriage, too, for Ron would remain working in New York City. But after talking with my father, I was even more convinced that I was doing the right thing. Not for Ron. Not for me. But for our children.

"Dad," I said, signaling an end to our conversation, "I really don't know how this will play out, but I know we have to make the change now, before the kids get too old and settled. It will be all right. Ron's a good man. I married him because I know that he'll always put his family first. We'll work it out. And it will be nice to live near you and Mom again."

I stood up to check on Eric who was napping in an upstairs bedroom as my dad, shaking his head slightly, reached out for the crossword puzzle book lying on the table beside his recliner.

Upstairs, I adjusted the quilt that covered Eric and gently touched his cheek with the back of my index finger. I knew that I had told my father only part of the truth. It was true: I did want my children to be raised in New England, near my family. But my urgency to move back had another reason, one I hadn't wanted to discuss. By moving back I hoped my children could get to know their grandparents well before that opportunity disappeared. Downstairs, I could hear my father talking with my mother, his voice raspy and hoarse, his vocal chords permanently damaged by radiation administered the year before for throat cancer. He was still in remission—for how long was unclear. It was time to come home.

FOUR / Psychotic Break

W E MOVED TO CONCORD, Massachusetts three months after our daughter Katie was born, and my family immediately embraced us. Ginny and her children helped us unpack on our first evening home, an older niece offered to babysit for us that first summer, and my brother-in-law began construction on our new home. My parents, too, were elated to have us living in a neighboring community and they spent our first summer home spoiling their youngest grandchildren. Unfortunately, our honeymoon was short-lived.

Six months after our return, my father had a heart attack and was immediately scheduled for heart surgery; after sixty years of smoking, every artery near his heart needed to be bypassed. Then, a few weeks later, my sister Ginny called. It was late, my children were already asleep, and Ginny told me that Mom wasn't doing well. She hadn't been sleeping at night and was showing signs of paranoia, insisting, for example, that a slightly burnt piece of macaroni served at lunch was a piece of wood someone had slipped into her meal. Summoned by my father that evening, Ginny was heading to my parents' home and wanted me to help bring Mom to a hospital. I didn't press Ginny for details or question her judgment. Both she and her husband, Jon, have years of experience in mental health; if Ginny said my mother needed to go to the hospital, I deferred to her judgment. When I arrived at their house, I found my mother glassy-eyed and physically rigid, spouting gibberish and losing touch with reality. Instead of calling for an ambulance as we had in the past, we decided to drive her to Mount Auburn Hospital, thinking it was better to have her medical and psychiatric care coordinated in one place.

After several failed attempts to get her into the car, Ginny told Mom that Dr. Harmon wanted to see her and, to our surprise, she went willingly, never questioning why the doctor wanted to see her at eleven o'clock in the evening. My father, still recovering from heart surgery and clearly relieved to have us handle my mother's care, remained at home. I drove the car while Ginny sat in the backseat next to Mom, engaging her in a chatty conversation to distract her until we reached the emergency room. We expected that she would be evaluated promptly and placed in a bed in their psychiatric unit.

The physicians on duty were young but articulate and professional. They first had to rule out any medical cause of her psychosis. They ordered lab tests and carefully explained each procedure. The hours wore on as we awaited the test results and then had a consult with a psychiatrist. My mother was agitated but stayed in bed. The doctors spoke kindly to her, explaining the reason for any delays; her psychosis didn't seem to bother them.

At six o'clock in the morning, we were finally told what would happen next: she was going to be transferred to the psychiatric unit at Beechman Hospital, in one of the poorest and most violent sections of Boston. We were stunned and Ginny was furious. We had brought our mother to Mount Auburn Hospital instead of Melrose-Wakefield Hospital so that she could be treated there. We had hoped that we could combine her care in one facility, with her internist collaborating with a psychiatrist about her treatment just as he collaborated with other specialists for her medical care. That Dr. Harmon had approved the transfer only increased our dismay.

I was tired and upset. I found a telephone and called Ron to tell him about my mother's placement. He was outraged too.

"They're going to send her to Beechman?" he asked incredulously. "You must be kidding. How are you going to see her? And what about your father? He just had open-heart surgery. He can't travel that far from home."

"Well," I replied wearily, "they don't have a bed available here."

"You cannot let them send her to Beechman Hospital."

"I don't think I have any choice. The ambulance is on its way."

"You have to stop the transfer," he persisted, ignoring my remarks.

"Really?" I replied. "What should I do, lie down in the driveway to stop the ambulance?"

I shook my head, groggy from lack of sleep. This was not what I had expected to hear from Ron. Stop the transfer? How? The doctors seemed to be handling my mother's case properly, with the right balance of compassion and skill. They had ruled out medical issues, called in a psychiatric consult, and had found a bed for her. Now the ambulance was on its way and I was supposed to accept their decision. But something was wrong. Ginny was angry, Ron was upset, and my head was so foggy that I couldn't think straight. I leaned back against the cement wall of the hospital, my eyes stinging.

Ron was telling me to stop the transfer and I needed to listen to him. I knew that he and his family had worked for decades within the medical system trying to negotiate decent care for his father, who lived with multiple sclerosis. I knew most of their stories of missteps and mistreatment; Ron also had an uncle and a brother who were physicians. I needed to trust him. I needed to stop the transfer.

"Why Beechman?" Ron asked. Without question, my mother needed care in a psychiatric unit. But there were at least a dozen choices within twenty miles of Boston. Why had they chosen Beechman? Something wasn't right. "They must think that she's a Medicaid patient."

"How can they think that?" I said, dismissing this. "She has been coming to Mount Auburn for years. They should know that she has good health insurance."

Although my parents' pension check was modest, my father had retired with the platinum card of health insurance: Medicare and Federal Blue Cross and Blue Shield. The fees one insurance policy didn't cover, the other did. My parents paid zero in hospital and medical bills. Nada. Nothing. I had been stunned the first time I saw my father receive a statement from Medicare after I asked him if he wanted me to track payments. "Don't bother," he had said. "I just file them away." Ron and I often joked that our next job would be working for the federal government, and we knew quite well why our Congressmen were slow to act on a national insurance policy: they never have to deal with health insurance payments.

"I'm telling you, they think she's on Medicaid," Ron insisted. "Why else would they choose Beechman? You must tell them that she can afford better care than that. She can't go there, Jan. She'll die there."

I felt a wave of nausea roll from head to toe. Die? The room darkened and my stomach sank. It was the wrong choice, and I knew now I should have intervened earlier. I shut my eyes and said almost in a whisper, "Ron, I think it may be too late. The ambulance will be here any minute."

Ron was silent, and I let him think for me. I was too exhausted to consider the alternatives.

"Wasn't she in a private hospital before?" he asked, reminding me of her placement at the Charles River Hospital years ago. "Tell them she is not going to Beechman. If they won't find another hospital, insist on a private placement, even if we have to pay for it."

"We might have to," I cautioned.

"So we'll pay. I don't care what it costs, Jan, she cannot go to Beechman Hospital. Just stop her from going there."

"Okay," I replied with more confidence than I had. "I'll do my best."

I hung up the telephone, closed my eyes, and took a deep breath. I felt like David, loading my slingshot with pebbles to stop the giant Goliath. The ambulance was on its way, and in only a few minutes, my mother would be taken from my grasp.

Our first encounter with the mental health system had occurred seventeen years before. At the time, we knew little about mental health care. Instead, we preferred to look for a medical cause: maybe it was the side effect of medication or a small stroke. Our denial was enabled by medical professionals who either could not or would not call it as it was.

This was her fourth breakdown, and we were still no further along in developing a game plan for managing these episodes. Each episode was treated as a discrete event by her physicians, precipitated by some unknown medical crisis. Dr. Harmon, who had been following both her and my father's medical care for ten years, had done little to intervene in her mental health care. When my father had throat cancer, Dr. Harmon arranged for a medical consult and cutting-edge treatment at Massachusetts General Hospital; when my dad needed bypass surgery and my mother needed a pacemaker, the cardiologists were called and the surgery was scheduled; and if this had been another medical emergency, she would have been on her way upstairs to a bed in one of the medical units. Instead, because it was a mental health issue, he was allowing my mother to be shipped to another institution, miles away from home, into the care of unknown physicians. It was heartbreaking, but I knew that I didn't have time to be upset.

I walked toward the nursing station. Taking advantage of a lull in activity, the three physicians were writing up their notes from the evening's cases. They were preparing to go off shift. They had put in a long evening and were likely anxious to go home. I hesitated. I had always deferred to the doctors, assuming that they knew best, and I preferred that my sister Ginny handle the mental health issues: she drew upon decades of experience working with children and adults with special needs. As I moved closer to the nurses' station, I realized that I had no idea what I was going to say. I simply had to stop this transfer. I walked over to the desk and spoke to the nearest physician.

"Excuse me," I began politely. "I understand that you want to send my mother to Beechman."

"Yes," he replied pleasantly, "the ambulance is on its way."

"She can't go there," I said as assertively as I could. He arched his brow and looked at the others seated behind the desk. They appeared to find their notes particularly engrossing.

"Look," I continued before I lost my nerve, "my father just had open-heart surgery here three weeks ago. You can check the records. He and my mother have been Dr. Harmon's patients for years and have been treated here many times. We brought her here to be evaluated because we thought it would be the best place for her. There's a psychiatric unit at Mount Auburn and it makes more sense for her to be treated in familiar territory than to go into a new hospital. Who's going to care for her at Beechman?"

His demeanor did not change. "Unfortunately, our unit is full," he said empathetically. "We don't have a bed for her here."

I drew in a long, slow breath.

"I understand that, but Beechman? Don't you understand that we won't be able to help her there?" I couldn't bear the thought of my mother waking from her confused state alone, thinking that we didn't care enough to be there beside her. "The best place for her," I said firmly, "is Melrose-Wakefield Hospital. It's a community hospital about twenty minutes from my parents' home. She has been there before; they have her records too."

The doctor did not respond to my suggestion.

I felt a twinge of anger.

"Is this an insurance question? If she's going to Beechman because you think she's on Medicaid, you have made a mistake. She has Medicare and Federal Blue Cross and Blue Shield insurance. That information should be in your database. It's the best insurance coverage that exists; it covers psychiatric care," I said, not knowing for sure if that was true. "I don't understand why you chose Beechman. Isn't that a state mental institution?"

I find it difficult to describe what happened next, for my reaction was so out of character that to this day I have spoken about it only once.

My mother's physician hesitated, and my mind, now fully awake, felt acutely ill at ease. Perhaps it was the flicker of surprise on his face when I mentioned her insurance. Perhaps it was the reaction of the other doctors, still seated but now listening, engrossed in our conversation. Perhaps it was Ron's insistence that they thought my mother was a Medicaid patient. Whatever the source of my discomfort, there was something about the way he responded—or, rather, did not respond—that pushed my mind into overdrive.

Why Beechman? My mind searched frantically for the answer, stumbling like a drunk in the dark, searching for the light switch. My mother was not a stranger; she did not walk in off the streets for treatment. She had a relationship with this hospital, a physician on staff who cared for both her and my father. She had the best health insurance available and two daughters by her side. What was wrong? How had they made this decision, a decision that I, as the patient's daughter, was supposed to accept?

That decision was unacceptable. *Stop the transfer.*

Suddenly, I found the light switch and was nearly blinded by the truth. These physicians, unconsciously or not, had profiled my mother. She was frail, elderly, and seriously ill. She was from Woburn, not Wellesley, a woman of modest means, in need of acute mental health care. Psychiatric care is expensive and often not covered by insurance. Instinctively I knew, and would later confirm, that they did not know that she had Federal health insurance. Why did that matter? Why did they not ask us about her choices and options? The answer was elusive, the ambulance on its way. *Stop the transfer.*

A wave of understanding rose over me as I realized that the system had made that choice, without input or discussion, because my mother was powerless.

Powerless. The twinge of anger I had felt when the physician ignored my suggestion to move her to Melrose-Wakefield Hospital now burst into flames. In that moment, I understood and I felt the injustice in the health care system, a system where quality of care is triaged by age, education, or ability to pay for services, for patients who are powerless to change the decisions of the doctors in whom they trust.

My heart lurched and I reacted instantaneously. My right hand reached into my pocketbook as I turned to the doctor.

"This isn't what it seems," I said coldly, my eyes venomous and blazing but my voice steady and calm. *I can't believe that I have to do this to get the right placement for her.* I could feel my body tighten; I inhaled slowly to diffuse the anger.

My hand found the edge of the checkbook in my purse. "My mother is not going to Beechman. There are better choices." I pulled out the checkbook and set it on the counter. "If you are worried about insurance, then whatever her health insurance won't cover, my husband and I will. I'll pay upfront if that's required and I will sign any document you need to guarantee payment." The other physicians looked up and made no pretense about ignoring the conversation. "I am not kidding."

I was appalled by what I was doing and overwhelmed by exhaustion and worry. Yet as I spoke, I knew that it was right to intervene. My mother was powerless; I was not. I was not David grappling for stones. I had a cannon, and I was going to use it. Drawing up to full height, I gazed steadily into the attending physician's eyes.

"*My* mother," I repeated with deadly precision, "is *NOT* going to Beechman."

There was silence.

Silence. What was he thinking? Thirty more minutes and he'd be off duty. Sleepy and tired, he probably just wanted to go home.

Silence. He was intelligent and articulate, but perhaps he had never had a family question his judgment, so willing to pay cash, up front, to correct it.

Silence. His eyes lingered on the checkbook. Did he wonder who I might know? A well-connected patient, who surely could make trouble at the start of his career?

Silence. He seemed unable to respond. Perhaps it was something more visceral: a sudden, unexpected confrontation with a lioness, powerful and poised to protect her cub, and rip him to shreds.

I tried to soften my outburst. "Please," I continued, "My sister and I are at our wits' end. I have two small children, one and four years old. My sister has four kids. We both work. We're trying to care for our father who is at home alone right now recovering from open-heart surgery. And you're going to send our mother to Beechman? She'll be left alone. We...won't...be...able...to help her. Please, aren't there other choices?"

More silence followed; I held my breath.

It was the female physician who spoke first. "You say she's been at Melrose-Wakefield before?"

"Yes," I responded, turning to her and ignoring the other two. "I'm sure they'll take her if they have a bed." It would require a few telephone calls, but she seemed willing to stay a few minutes past her shift to help.

"And she has Federal Blue Cross insurance?"

"Yes. The number should be in Mount Auburn's database, but if you don't have it, let me get her insurance card."

I quickly returned to my mother's side before they had a change of heart.

It seemed like hours had passed since I went to call my husband. My sister Ginny was waiting. She looked at me quizzically. "I don't think they knew she had Federal insurance," I said simply. "They're going to look into other options."

Two hours later, my mother was on her way to the psychiatric unit in Melrose-Wakefield Hospital. Later that night I spoke to Ginny on the telephone.

"We're going to work with these doctors to get a game plan together for Mom. If Dr. Harmon can't handle her, we'll find someone who can. You and I will never stay up all night again to get her the help she needs."

I was so naïve.

FIVE / Financial Control

YEARS LATER, I would ask a social worker for her opinion about the incident at Mount Auburn. Is our medical system so broken that only elders with resources can get decent health care? I told her that my husband and I could have put my mother into a private hospital, but most families do not have that choice; I found the thought disturbing. The social worker replied that what was most important was that I had advocated for my mother, not that I had offered to pay for services. According to her, a patient advocate, a hollow phrase until then, is what most elders with chronic or terminal illnesses need to successfully navigate the health care system.

Without full awareness of my new role, the incident at Mount Auburn was a turning point in my involvement with my mother's health care. Although much of my time was booked with consulting projects, preschoolers, and the hectic life of two working parents, I resolved that she would never again navigate the medical system alone. Ginny would continue to do her part, but now I would be involved as well. My father, struggling with his own medical issues, would have our active and steadfast support.

Ginny followed my mother's treatment during her stay at Melrose-Wakefield Hospital. After my mother was released, a psychiatrist named Dr. Christakos began to manage her care. A large man with a gentle manner, he scheduled counseling sessions with my parents. I offered to drive them to the sessions and sit in on the meetings to take notes. I was determined to establish a relationship with Dr. Christakos so that we could treat my mother properly if she had future episodes.

To be honest, my mother's behavior disturbed me. Until the

incident at Mount Auburn, I had gladly let Ginny manage her care. I coped best by dealing with each episode in the moment and later acting as if nothing unusual had occurred. The glassy eyes, the gibberish, the physical outbursts: she was so out of control one minute and then, just a few weeks later, completely normal again. I wasn't ashamed of my mother—I just couldn't handle it. Ginny seemed to both understand and accept what was happening. I was at a loss.

Through our meetings with Dr. Christakos, however, I came to see my mother's illness as just that, another illness. Like asthma, diabetes, or heart disease, this was an illness that could be controlled by daily medication. And like other chronic diseases, there would be times when the medication would not work, and a brief stay in the hospital with supplementary care and medication would correct the problem.

My mother's illness was diagnosed as depression. The blues we casually noticed in the spring and the fall are classic symptoms, and her breakdowns, called psychotic breaks, are not uncommon. Left untreated, depression can lead to significant changes in a part of the brain called the hippocampus, which can lead to cumulative episodes of depression with psychosis.

It seemed that these episodes had started when she was fifty-eight years old, the year I moved out of her home. While she certainly experienced severe depression following the deaths of her sister and mother, the demands of raising a large family and our old family physician's advice to "make a pot of tea and put your feet up" left her alone to push through the trenches. Her age was also a factor. It is believed that levels of serotonin, a hormone considered a natural sleep aid that helps to regulate mood, decreases with age, and elderly people therefore experience depression more often than other age groups. Of course, the elderly tend to have more to be depressed about as their own bodies weaken and spouses, friends, and family members experience serious medical crises and loss. Dr. Christakos gave my mother Paxil, a mild antidepressant well tolerated by elderly patients. When hospitalized, she had been given two antipsychotic drugs: first, Haldol, to calm her mind, and later, Risperdal. She took Paxil daily, along with her heart medications and vitamins.

We wanted my mother to find another internist. Dr. Harmon's absence from her care at Mount Auburn was unforgivable. He seemed capable of handling physical ailments but incapable of managing mental health ones; we needed someone to treat both. We urged our parents to change doctors but they would have none of it. They had been Dr. Harmon's patients for years and felt comfortable with his care. To his credit, he had done an exceptional job with their physical care.

We knew that having an internist in one hospital and a psychiatrist in another was a prescription for trouble. Inevitably, an explosion occurred. The clash would happen two years later concerning my father's care.

*   *   *

One morning, the telephone in my home office rang.

"Have you talked with Dad today?" Ginny asked, getting right to the reason for her call.

"No," I replied, knowing that either she or one of her four daughters called our parents daily. "Why, what's up?"

"Dad went to the doctor to check on a pain in his chest. He thought he might have pneumonia. They took an x-ray. Jan, they found lung cancer."

"Damn," I said and I shut my eyes, pressing the telephone receiver against my forehead, my left hand absently rubbing my temple. After a long pause, I found my voice. "I'd like to say I'm surprised, but Ginny, he's been smoking for more than sixty years. I guess it was inevitable."

"I guess. Well, you'd better call him. Soon."

I hung up the telephone and saved my work on the computer. The telephone rang again.

"Jan." It was my father.

"Hi Dad, Ginny just told me the news." I purposely avoided the word cancer. "It sounds like they caught it in the early stages, though."

"Yeah, I think they did. I have to go through some more tests, but they should be able to remove the bad lung."

"Well, good," I replied, trying to sound encouraging.

"But listen," he interrupted, "I just got off the telephone with Henry Johnson, our lawyer, do you remember him? He's going to draw up some papers for me. Your mother is going to need help, paying bills and all of that. She's not going to be able to handle everything on her own. Would you mind helping her out?"

"Of course not," I said, "And let me know when your medical appointments are scheduled. I'll take you to them."

"Are you going to have time?" he asked.

"Sure," I promised. I had just started a new project to restructure the marketing department of a regional bank with $30 billion in assets, but he didn't know that. "I can shuffle my meetings around if I need to. You just let me know when your appointments are scheduled."

"Thanks," he said. He seemed relieved.

"I'll be over sometime this week and you can show me what I need to know about the bills. When you have a few minutes, why don't you pull all the information together?" If nothing else, it might keep him occupied and distracted.

The enormity of his decision struck me only after I hung up the telephone. My father had just asked his lawyer to draft a legal document called a durable power of attorney. A durable power of attorney is typically written for people with a terminal illness, like cancer, or dementing illnesses, such as Alzheimer's and Parkinson's diseases. It gives the person named broad power to manage someone's financial assets. With that document in place, I could pay their bills, sell their house, take out loans, access their safe deposit box, and conduct any number of financial transactions on their behalf. Unlike a standard power of attorney document, the durable power of attorney gave me that authority even if he or my mother, since she would sign a similar document, were declared mentally incapacitated.

My father knew that lung cancer was a death sentence. Although he had confronted death before, this time would be different; I could hear that in his voice, a false bravado I wasn't used to hearing from him. He knew that he would eventually lose this battle. I stared at the computer screen, elbows on my desk, and rubbed my forehead absentmindedly. My dad was worried: worried enough to pick up the telephone immediately after scheduling surgery to ask his lawyer to draw up papers; worried enough to check his pride and ask for my help in paying the bills and running their household; worried enough to ask me to help take care of Mom. He was too proud to ask for my help for himself, he'd be a stubborn Irishman to his death, but his love for my mother would not allow him to brave this storm with her unprotected. I felt my eyes well. He could have asked any of his children for help; I was deeply touched by his confidence in me.

*   *   *

Later that week I stopped by their house for a cup of tea. While my mother puttered around upstairs, my father and I moved into the dining room. This was the room where I had eaten supper every night as a child and where spouses and grandchildren lingered for hours over our regular Sunday dinners. Out of habit, I headed to the right of my father at the head of the table, a placement assigned to me decades before because of my left-handedness. He opened a loose-leaf notebook, its blue fabric cover fraying at the edges. Clipped to the cover were documents from the National Association of Retired Federal Employees. Inside, written mostly in my mother's handwriting on the wide-ruled notebook paper, were the account numbers and details of their pension, five insurance policies, two charge cards, seven stocks, six bank accounts, three certificates of deposit, and twenty-three savings bonds. Their entire financial portfolio was recorded on sixteen bits of paper.

"This looks good," I said seriously. "It's helpful to have everything in one place. Do you know how much money you have in total?"

"No," he said honestly, "but it's all listed there."

"Do you mind if I borrow this notebook, just for the week? I can put all of this onto my computer, which will make it easier to track everything. You know, today a computer will do all the math calculations. I'll get the information organized and show you the spreadsheet. I think you'll like it."

"Sounds good."

"Now, what about the bills?"

"Well, that's your mother's territory."

He went over to the desk and unlocked the cabinet.

"She keeps the bills in here and pays them once a week. Here's the checkbook, and she also records each bill by month in this spiral notebook." He handed me a spiral notebook and I flipped through its pages, filled with neat columns of numbers in my mother's handwriting. I laid her notebook on top of my father's messy pile of loose-leaf papers.

"What are you doing in the desk?" my mother demanded, coming downstairs into the living room. She had been making the beds upstairs.

"I'm just showing Jan where you keep the checkbook," my dad replied meekly.

"Now, Bob, you know I don't like anyone touching my bills."

"Murie," he said using an endearing term, trying to calm her down, "Jan is just going to help us."

"We don't need her help!"

"Mom," I interceded, for diplomacy was not my father's strong suit, "I'm not going to touch your bills or your checkbook. Dad is just showing me where things are in case you both get busy running to the doctors and need someone to pay a bill or two someday. Don't worry, the checkbook and the notebook will stay in your desk. I'll come over here, whenever you need help, if you need help, and we can pay the bills together. You can show me what to do if that time comes."

She furrowed her brow and walked away, unconvinced.

"We'll have to go to the bank so you can put me on your account," I said quietly after she left the room. "It's really not a big deal, Dad. I can be the third signatory. My name doesn't even need to appear on the checks." We made plans to get that done between medical appointments.

In the subsequent weeks, our attention focused on completing the medical tests required in anticipation of surgery. Despite smoking his entire life, a critical test of his lung capacity found he could support life using just one lung. He had walked four to five miles daily for nearly fifteen years with some old cronies in the neighborhood. That exercise and his overall strong physiology were now paying dividends.

My oldest brother, Bill, attended the last appointment with the surgeon and gave me some journal articles about lung cancer. During the appointment, we had pressed the surgeon for details about his quality of life after surgery, but the doctor evaded the questions, only committing to the fact that he would be able to sit up in a chair and breathe on his own. Not a promising vision, but we'd take it.

The journal articles prompted me to call a friend, Mary Simon, about my father's treatment. At that time, Mary ran global marketing research for Bristol-Myers Squibb's Pharmaceutical Division and had phenomenal recall of clinical data and statistics. A brilliant woman with a wicked sense of humor, her favorite joke was "What do they call the person who graduates at the bottom of his or her medical school class?" Pause, for effect: "Doctor."

After some small talk, I got right to the point, telling Mary about my father's recent diagnosis of lung cancer and providing her with a brief medical history. "He's having a lung removed, but they have not scheduled radiation or chemotherapy. I'm trying to figure out if I should push for that, but I thought I would check with you first."

It might seem strange that I would ask for medical advice from a marketing research executive as opposed to a physician. Most of the knowledge that physicians acquire, however, is based on clinical studies reported in medical journals or symposia. Clinical studies, conducted by physicians and medical researchers at the major teaching hospitals across America, are used to evaluate treatment choices for specific diseases and medical conditions. The funding for these studies comes from two sources: the government, through the National Institutes of Health, or from major pharmaceutical and biotech companies. At the time, Bristol-Myers Squibb had the largest oncology practice of all the pharmaceutical companies, and Mary had access to all of the current research.

"Do you know of any studies done comparing outcomes both

with and without chemotherapy and radiation?" I asked. *Outcomes*, I mused, using a term that physicians and researchers loved. *Such a nice way to avoid saying "death rates."* I could hear her brain cells whirring through the receiver.

"Well," she said thoughtfully, "I recall one study with ten thousand patients that tracked outcomes following different treatments." She cited the name of the study and the researchers. I couldn't help but smile: she was brilliant. Mary continued to cite the study protocol and findings. "The study concluded that the treatment protocol did not statistically impact patient outcomes."

"In other words," I said quietly, "it doesn't matter."

"Yes, unfortunately, that's right."

"Okay, I didn't think so, and I certainly don't want him to spend the last months of his life suffering unnecessarily. The side effects of chemo and radiation can be pretty nasty." I paused to push the image out of my mind.

"Mary," I said. "I need to ask you one last thing. What did the study say about longevity? I really need to know how much time he has left. This isn't only about my father. My mother is also not well, and I have to set things up properly for her. I really need to know if I have three months or three years. Based on the studies, what's your best guess?"

There was silence, and I braced myself for her answer. I wasn't ready to find out how much time I had left with my father: no one's ever ready to hear that, but I knew that she would do what my father's physicians had avoided. She would tell me the statistical probability of his survival.

"He'll have a year, maybe a year and a half."

I felt my heart drop. I shut my eyes and took a deep, slow breath. A year of living goes by so quickly; I wondered what a year of dying would feel like.

After a pause to regain my composure, I thanked Mary and hung up the telephone. For the first time, after years of denial, I let myself feel that my father was going to die.

SIX / Hallucinations

I ACCOMPANIED MY FATHER and mother to the hospital on the day of his lung surgery. When we arrived, as part of the admissions process, my father was given a clipboard of documents to sign. One paper was a health care proxy, a legal document that gives the person named, typically a family member, the authority to make all health care decisions for a patient if he or she is unable to express his or her wishes. While the document applies to a wide range of decisions, from treatment choices to nursing home placement, its most significant use is in the decision to terminate life support. Lung surgery is a high-risk operation and, according to the clerk, the hospital would not operate on my father unless he signed the health care proxy. A flash of fear crossed my father's face as he looked at me worriedly.

"Jan," he said signing the document and handing it to me, "don't give up on me." I took the form and recorded my mother's name as the health care agent, with me as the alternate. The proxy underscored the gravity of his operation.

"You know better than that, Dad," I replied reassuringly. "You're the cat with nine lives and this is only number six or seven. You'll do fine with one lung." I handed the clipboard back to the clerk.

"Besides, don't worry," I continued, winking at the nurse, "Only the good die young."

"Well, in that case, I'm all set." He relaxed noticeably, and we resumed an easy banter, not allowing the proxy to dampen our upbeat mood.

One of my father's greatest assets was his ability to find irony and humor in the gravest of circumstances. The worse things got, the funnier he became, cracking jokes, telling stories, making the

41

nurses and doctors and interns and everyone else around laugh. It was a trait that had rubbed off on our entire family. My father and his brothers were hysterically funny, low-keyed masters of the one-line quip, and it was only when I married into a family that copes with serious illnesses rather grimly that I realized laughter under stress was unusual.

The weeks following my father's lung surgery were busy ones. Everyone in the family pitched in to help accommodate my father. My brother Walter and I transformed my parents' dining room into a bedroom since my father would not be able to climb stairs to the second floor bedrooms for at least a few months, if at all. My sisters arranged their work schedules so they could stay with my father overnight. And although visiting nurses were scheduled, my oldest sister, Carol, found home care, hiring nurses and aides to assist our parents when we were not available.

Not surprisingly, two weeks after my father returned home, Dr. Christakos admitted my mother to the psychiatric unit in Melrose-Wakefield Hospital for twelve days to recover from the strain. Her admission record noted that she had not been sleeping and that her weight, which had been a mere 112 pounds during her admission two years earlier, was now a frail 96 pounds. During her hospitalization, my husband and I took a long-planned one-week vacation with our children and Ginny's family in northern New Hampshire. Ron enjoyed time with our children and their cousins; I spent the week squirreled away with my laptop, finishing a PowerPoint presentation for a client. By the end of our vacation, I could barely climb the small driveway between our condominium and the clubhouse. I was physically and mentally exhausted.

"I think this is going to be my last assignment for a while," I told Ron one night after dinner. "If my father only has one year left, I'd like to spend it with him, undistracted by my work. Do you mind?"

"Mind? Honestly Jan, I don't know why you've kept consulting this long anyway. Take a break. You know you can always go back."

Despite Ron's assurances, I was worried about taking time off. I knew, though, that my colleagues would find assignments without me, giving me the time I needed to support my father. I felt grateful for the ability to have this choice. A few years earlier, I would never have considered that the shift away from a full-time job to spend more time with my children would now also give me the flexibility I needed to support my elderly parents. That September, my children started first grade and preschool; for the first time in years, I had a few hours free each morning. At first, I stopped in at my parents' home daily to ensure that they were coping adequately. Within a couple of months, my father's health improved such that he no longer needed nursing care. We hired a companion to help with the housework, to run errands, and to cook. I knew my mother had recovered from her last episode when she started complaining about the money being spent on the hired help.

"Muriel," my father told her, "I know you don't want to spend the money, but we need a little help. I don't want you to do everything for me. Remember, we saved our pennies for a rainy day, and right now, it's pourin'!"

"Yep," I replied nodding. "It's hurricane season."

My father smiled sadly and my mother dropped the subject, at least until my next visit. Her persistence was a good sign. After observing her behavior for a few weeks more, I cut the companion's schedule from five to three days each week, figuring I could fill in the gaps if needed.

*　*　*

Six months following the surgery, my parents seemed settled in their routines, but my father's good humor seemed to have faded with the frequent trips to the doctor and a near obsession with his physical ailments.

"Dad seems really down," I said to Ginny one afternoon. "He's becoming such a poop."

"I wouldn't use that word," she said laughing.

"You're right, if I have to listen to one more story about his intestinal troubles, I am going to scream! I guess he is just getting old."

One morning, I stopped by my parents' house to take my mother to her appointment with Dr. Christakos. While she was upstairs getting ready, I sat at the kitchen table with my dad enjoying a cup of tea.

"So, Mom seems to be doing okay lately," I said. "How are you doing?"

"I don't know," he said. "I'm so nervous and I don't know why."

"Well, Dad, you've been through a lot these past few years. First you had throat cancer, then heart surgery, and now lung surgery. You're a tough old bird, but that's not easy to handle. Add Mom on top of that, and you've really had your hands full."

"Yeah," he nodded, "but I shouldn't be this nervous."

"What does Dr. Harmon think?"

"He told me that I can increase the pills I'm taking to four times a day."

"Let me look at your schedule," I said going to the counter where they kept their pill charts. For years my parents kept a simple table of their medications on a writing tablet. In the left column, they listed their medications and in the right were spaces to check off each tablet daily as it was taken. The pill chart was a useful way for them to keep track of the pills they had taken and to remember the names of the pills when they visited the doctor.

I took his pill tray out of the cabinet and looked at the bottle. For the first time, I noted the dosing of his medication: he was taking two 30-milligram tablets daily. The doctor now said he could take four tablets, which would be 120 milligrams of medication. By contrast, my mother was taking only 20 milligrams of Paxil each day. Common sense told me that maybe he needed to switch pills: if my mother's chronic depression could be controlled by only 20 milligrams of medicine, did he really need six times that amount to handle a little anxiety?

Later that morning, after Dr. Christakos finished talking to my mother, he turned to me and asked, "Do you have any questions?" I had decided to ask him my about my father's medicine, for his experience as a psychiatrist and training in psychopharmacology likely surpassed Dr. Harmon's knowledge about antianxiety drugs.

"Not about my mother," I replied. "She seems to be doing very well, but I am a bit concerned about my father. He's taking some medication for anxiety, but it doesn't seem to be working."

"Oh?" he responded politely. "What is he taking?"

"Something called Serax," I replied. "His doctor wants to increase the dosing to 120 milligrams a day."

Dr. Christakos seemed surprised by the choice of drug.

"Serax is a powerful drug," he told me. "We use it in our alcohol detoxification program for maybe three to four days to help patients cope with withdrawal symptoms. Then we switch to something milder. How long has your father been taking Serax?"

I adjusted my seat so I could observe his reaction. I knew that psychiatrists, of all doctors, are well schooled at managing their personal reactions. I wanted a clear view of his face and I wanted to see his body language.

"Two-and-a-half years," I replied nonchalantly.

He nearly jumped out of his skin.

"What? Did you say years?" he asked incredulously.

"Yes," I replied. "I believe it was first prescribed for him following his bypass surgery. That was two-and-a-half years ago."

Dr. Christakos was silent for a moment.

"Serax, or oxazepam," he began, "belongs to a class of drugs called the benzodiazepines that are typically prescribed for short-term use to address anxiety, insomnia, or acute psychosis. Although elders better tolerate Serax than some other drugs in this class, I typically avoid using them with my elderly patients. Older people are more sensitive than younger patients to the depressant effects of the benzodiazepines, partly because they metabolize drugs less efficiently than younger people, so the drug effects last longer and drug accumulation readily occurs with regular use." He paused briefly, as if aware suddenly that I might not understand what he was saying. I understood every word.

"So," I asked, "what should I do for him?"

"You may know," he continued, "that when someone starts taking an antidepressant, you do not see an immediate effect on mood. In fact, it typically takes at least three to four weeks to show an appreciable clinical effect. For similar reasons, your father cannot abruptly stop using Serax or he may experience unpleasant withdrawal symptoms. The dosing will need to be tapered off slowly."

In other words, I thought, *after taking Serax for so long, Dad is like a drug addict.* I was furious, but held my tongue. Dr. Christakos offered to consult with Dr. Harmon about a withdrawal protocol that would safely remove the drug from his system. I offered my thanks and took my mother home.

Later that day I called Ginny to tell her what Dr. Christakos had said.

"We have to get Dad off that drug, but Dr. Harmon probably won't do it," I warned.

"Then we'll go around him," Ginny responded tartly.

I took my father to his next appointment with Dr. Harmon and sat in on the office discussion. Before discussing his medications, they first covered his concerns about his intestinal troubles. When the time came, I watched as my father weakly explained Dr. Christakos' comments. Dr. Harmon was obviously miffed that his advice was being questioned. While I said little, I left the office determined to get my dad off Serax with, or without, Dr. Harmon's help.

A few days later, I stopped by my parents' house.

"Your father said that Dr. Harmon doesn't want him for a patient anymore," my mother reported, obviously distressed.

"What?" I said, flabbergasted by the doctor's response to a little criticism.

"Yes, Dad said that Dr. Harmon called and told him he doesn't want to keep us as patients."

"Well, don't worry Mom," I said, now hopeful that they would accept us finding another primary care physician. "If Dr. Harmon has a problem with us questioning his medical judgment, we'll deal with it. First we have to get Dad weaned off of this Serax."

The following day Ginny called.

"Did Mom tell you that the neighbors want them to move out of the neighborhood?"

"What?" My parents had lived in their neighborhood for nearly fifty years.

"Yeah, I guess Dad said that Marjorie wants them to move."

"Oh, cripes. No, I didn't hear that. Mom told me that Dr. Harmon doesn't want them as patients any more, but now I don't know if that is the truth. Don't tell me that she's starting to act up again. I can't handle two of them. We'll have to keep a better eye on them."

A few days later, Ginny called again and insisted Dad stop taking Serax immediately. She told me he had been hallucinating: he thought that our brother-in-law Steve had come over the night before and smashed out every window in the garage with his hammer.

"Great," I said, "Now we have two of them out to lunch. You know this means more than just a drug change. They can't live alone if Dad loses it." Ginny agreed.

We brought my father to Dr. Christakos who agreed to oversee his withdrawal from Serax. Ginny also scheduled neuropsychological testing through the hospital's memory assessment clinic to determine if we were witnessing the start of his cognitive deterioration. By the time the day of his testing arrived, my father was off Serax and on 10 milligrams of Paxil. He seemed normal, but the test would tell us if it was only an illusion.

"How did it go?" we asked my father as he returned to the waiting room from his testing. Both Ginny and I had brought him to be tested.

"Well," my father said bemusedly, "that psychologist doesn't know his American history." An avid reader and history buff, my father had provided the psychologist, whose test must have included a few questions about American governance and history, with lengthy lectures about the Civil War and other historical events.

"Poor guy," I mumbled to Ginny, having experienced many of his long-winded dissertations. She nodded and laughed quietly.

During the family debriefing, the psychologist reported that my father's cognitive function was fine. His IQ tested in the 120s, and he had passed with flying colors.

Later I apologized to my father for insisting that he get tested.

"You know Dad, we're only comfortable with you two staying in your own home because we know that you're with it mentally. We're counting on you to tell us if something is going on with Mom. If you start losing it, you're going to have to come and live with me."

"Oh you don't want two old coots living with you, Jan," he said, with that familiar twinkle in his eye.

"No, I don't, really. But I'd rather have you living with me than worrying about you and Mom hurting yourselves inadvertently. Mom's forgetfulness is one thing, but you...?" I stopped, leaving the thought unfinished.

"Well, the truth is," he confided, "I forget things too, sometimes."

"Yeah, I know Dad, but everyone your age does. The difference is that you know that you're forgetful. Mom is forgetful, but she isn't aware."

"What do I tell Dr. Harmon?" he said, still worried about his relationship with the doctor. Despite Dr. Harmon's mistake with medication, my father insisted on keeping him as their physician.

"Just tell him the truth," I replied. "Tell him that Serax was causing you to hallucinate, and you had to get off of it. Blame us, if you need to. Tell him that you have two pushy middle-aged broads for daughters who will not take no for an answer. He'll let it go, but you can't take that drug again."

He nodded.

"Don't worry," I said soothingly, "Maybe we'll have Walter take you to the next appointment. He'll smooth things over, man-to-man, you know what I mean?" I laughed impishly, and his face broke into a wide grin. It was the first time I'd seen him smile in weeks.

My brother Walter brought my father to the next appointment, having been warned about the doctor's telephone call. Walter reported back that all was well. It turns out that the telephone call never happened; it was only a figment of my father's or my mother's imagination. To our chagrin, Dr. Harmon was still their primary care physician.

SEVEN / Caregiving Basics

MONTHS SLIPPED INTO A YEAR and my father's strength returned. He climbed stairs to sleep in his own bedroom, drove the car to run errands, and resumed his passion for crossword puzzles and reading. His improved health coincided with my mother's increasing annoyance toward the home companion. We decided to let the help go.

The decision to allow them to live alone again was not made lightly, but my parents now seemed to balance each other's abilities. On most days, my mother could cook, clean, and do the laundry; my father could drive her to the neighborhood grocery store for food shopping. Although she was somewhat forgetful, he was mentally sharp and could contact us for help in an emergency.

My parents also had an extensive, yet often invisible, network of support. Ginny and her daughters called daily and stopped by each Sunday for a visit. Ron and I brought our children over every Saturday night that we were in town. Walter took them out for breakfast every Thursday morning, creating such a comic uproar in the restaurant that the waitresses jostled for their table. I visited alone each Friday morning to pay bills, arrange their pills, and run quick errands. And my oldest sister, Carol, often stopped by after work. In addition to personal visits, my brothers and brothers-in-law kept an eye on home repairs while Ron maintained their car. Individually our contributions were minor, but collectively they ensured that their house was well maintained, there was food in the refrigerator, and their days were filled with laughter and companionship.

My parents also had watchful neighbors and friends. Pete Stanton, an unmarried elderly neighbor, walked the block five or six times daily, a local sentinel who spread the neighborhood gossip. My sister Carol's oldest friend lived across the street from our parents and watched for signs of trouble, particularly through the winter months. Their next door neighbors, Marjorie and John, stopped by almost daily for a quick chat, and countless church friends and neighbors dropped by intermittently. We had few concerns for their safety, left alone in their own home, for the constant flow of cars in their driveway and neighbors on the doorstep would keep any trouble at bay.

We also hired a friend who ran a house-cleaning business to clean their home for one hour each week. Her instructions from my mother, whose cleaning skills were legendary, were to vacuum the rugs, dust the furniture without breaking anything, and wash the kitchen floor. Our friend, though, would play a game of cat and mouse with my mother, cleaning the bathrooms when she was in another part of the house. My parents seemed content and capable at home, but I remained uneasy about the future. During one of my weekly visits, I raised the issue about giving up their house with my father.

"Would you like me to look into other living arrangements?" I asked gingerly. "It's a real nuisance to maintain your own house at this stage in life, and even though things are fine now, I could use this time to check out assisted living facilities and continuous care communities."

"No, Jan," he replied. "I looked at several a few years ago, but they're just too expensive. We can't afford to live in one of those places on our income."

"But aren't you worried about what might happen if you need serious help?" I pressed. "Most of the best facilities have waiting lists. In an emergency, you might not get into the facility that you want."

"Don't worry," he said grinning. "All I have to do is tell your brother Walter that I'm moving in with him. He'll get us into the Carleton-Willard Village the next week!" The Carleton-Willard Village was one of the best local continuous care communities.

"Dad, I'm not joking about this. I wish I could offer for you to move in with us, we have the space. But, frankly, I'm not sure that I could live with Mom. You, I could handle. But with Ron traveling all the time, I don't have anyone else to help me with Mom. And if she started having an episode with me alone with the kids, it could spell real trouble." He sat quietly and listened to me. "The kids are still little," I added, recalling her outbursts of physical aggression.

"Right now," I continued, unwilling to let the matter drop, "I have the time to check out some options. I might not have time later, especially if we're in the middle of a medical crisis."

He continued to sit reflectively.

"Look, Jan," he said finally. "I want to stay in my own house for as long as I can. If I get bad, I want you to put me in a nursing home. I do not want your mother trying to take care of me. But you must promise me this, do not sell the house out from under your mother. She must know that if something happens to me she can stay in her own house and she does not have to live with one of her kids. I want you to take whatever savings we have and spend it all on her care. All of it. We did what we could for you kids. You're all able to take care of yourselves. Spend our savings on her, hire whatever help she needs, and make sure she knows that she can stay here."

I nodded. I was reluctant to drop the subject but I let it go, leaving his and my mother's future housing unresolved. It was a decision, or rather an indecision, that I would later deeply regret.

*   *   *

Over time, we fell into an easy routine. Each Friday, I drove to their house with a supply of food, homemade soups, and chicken pie. I stopped at the local Dunkin' Donuts to retrieve their snacks—a lemon-filled donut for my father, a blueberry muffin for my mother, coffee for me. I retrieved the week's mail from the desk, sorted through it all, and paid the bills at the kitchen table. I then ran to the local pharmacy for their pills and stopped in the grocery store for any items they needed. We all looked forward to these few hours together.

Most weeks, my mother sniffed and snorted each time I paid their bills, but I came to view that as a sign of her good health. During her early seventies, she had spent close to a year purging their files and organizing their papers. As a result, all of their critical documents were either in their safe deposit box or in two file drawers. With little to organize, I simply recorded all of their financial information on a single spreadsheet, listing account numbers and balances for each of their savings or securities. It would take nearly a year to compile an accurate list. Some statements, like those for life insurance policies, only came through for payment once a year. The spreadsheet made management of their savings a snap. There was, however, the occasional surprise.

"What's this passbook, Dad?" I asked as I searched the desk for some stamps to mail their bills. "It only has Mom's name on it."

"Oh, that's your mother's mad money," he said, peering over his crossword puzzle.

"Mad money?" I asked. "What's that for? Isn't it a little late for her to think about running away?"

"She's always had her own money. She started that account right after the war when she saw a lot of young widows move back home with their parents. She wanted to have some money in case something happened to me. She didn't want to depend on anyone, and sometimes it takes a while to get things straightened out after someone dies."

"So why does she need it now?"

"It's her money," he said shrugging. "I never touch it."

I brought the passbook to the bank the next time I went; I gave ten dollars to the teller and asked her to update the account. I took the passbook and other papers and walked toward the exit, glancing casually at the register. I was floored.

When I got back home I asked my father if he knew how much money was in the passbook. He didn't.

"Twenty-three thousand dollars."

"Good for her," he said, disinterested.

"You're not going to let her keep it all in there, are you?" I asked incredulously.

"It's her money, Jan, I never touch it."

"Well, she can't let that kind of money stay in a passbook. I'm going to talk to her."

"Go ahead," he said, with a smirk on his face. "Good luck." He returned to his newspaper.

Over tea in the kitchen I told my mother I had taken her passbook to the bank to update the account. She eyed me coolly. I felt like she had caught me stealing.

"You have twenty-three thousand dollars in that account," I said. I had hoped to surprise her with the amount: after all, this was a woman who read the sale pages religiously each week and shopped for groceries in three stores to save a few pennies or dimes.

"Oh, really?" she said, almost as disinterested as my father had been. "That's nice."

I tried again. "Mom, that's a lot of money to keep in a passbook."

"It's my savings for a rainy day."

"I know, but it would have to rain for forty days and forty nights before you'd need that kind of money." She looked at me unsmiling. *It would be easier to negotiate world peace.* But I was not giving up. "Think about it. You can earn about 3 or 4 percent more each year by keeping your money in certificates of deposit rather than in a savings account. That means that you are giving up about a thousand dollars each year because you're leaving your money in a passbook. Mom, you already shop in three grocery stores to save a few dollars, why won't you shop in a couple of banks to save hundreds?"

She stared out the window.

"Listen," I said, reluctantly accepting defeat, "I know that you're concerned about having money if Dad dies. Worst-case scenario, you'll need five or six thousand dollars. So why don't you leave ten thousand dollars in the passbook and move the rest to a certificate of deposit?" I couldn't believe that I was willing to compromise with ten grand.

"Go ahead Jan," she said suddenly. "Do what you want with the money."

"I'll put the money in your name only, if you want," I said empathetically, understanding her need to keep her own separate funds.

"Oh don't be foolish," she replied haughtily, and she went downstairs to do the laundry, leaving me alone in the kitchen with my tea.

EIGHT / Celebrating Life

E VERY WEEK I LOOKED FORWARD to Friday morning with my father. Over tea we reconnected like lifelong friends, separated once by hundreds of miles, now together again at the kitchen table. We discussed politics and family, current events and history. I listened to him reminisce about the past and retell his favorite stories, embedding those stories into memory so I could pass them along to my children. I sought his advice on everything from growing tomatoes to raising boys, tapping into his nearly eighty years of acquired wisdom. I watched him stoically channel his stubborn Irish temperament into a fight to regain his strength and retain his independence; my admiration for him deepened. Often on those mornings, as his playful banter and pithy quips filled the kitchen with light and laughter, I forgot that he was dying. We never talked about his cancer: it was what it was, and he knew that whatever happened, we would deal with it, together, as a family. Today I know that these few hours each week with my father were my intermezzo, the interlude between two distinct stages of my life. As I sipped my tea and laughed at his stories, I could feel the self-absorption of my youth slipping away, replaced with the rich maturity of age. There was no one more capable of leading me through this transition than my father.

But, on occasion, his behavior was frustrating.

One Friday, Dad was in the middle of one of his stories when my mother stormed into the kitchen. "Shhh," she said sternly, "You're going to wake up the baby."

"What baby?" I asked, and I shot a quick glance at my dad. He was studying his tea cup.

"The baby is sleeping upstairs," she scolded. "Be quiet."

She went into the dining room and I could hear her raising and lowering the window shades. I continued paying the bills as my father picked up the story line, acting as if we had not been interrupted. *Whose child is here?* I was confused. A few minutes later, my mother strode up to the table.

"You have to be quiet," she insisted, "Mom is sleeping."

"Mom? Whose Mom? Are you telling me that your mother is upstairs sleeping?"

"Yes." Her mother had been dead for forty years.

"I see." I returned to the bills. A few minutes later, she went upstairs to make the beds.

"Dad," I whispered. "How long has she been like this?"

"A few days."

"Oh, for Pete's sake, why didn't you tell us?"

He looked away, staring sadly out the kitchen window. I stood up and walked around the kitchen table to his side, resting one hand gently on his shoulder, reaching above his head to take the telephone off its receiver. I found the office number for Dr. Christakos posted among the business cards and family telephone numbers on the bulletin board.

"Look, Dad," I said quietly, as I dialed the doctor's number. "I know that you don't want her to go into the hospital, but we can't keep her out of the hospital if you don't let us know when this starts." I left a three-part message on the doctor's answering machine: I explained that my mother was beginning to lose touch with reality again; I reminded him that he had used Risperdal during her last hospitalization; and I left the pharmacy number and asked him to call in the prescription so I could get her started on the medication. I promised to bring her in the next day for a consult. Within thirty minutes, Dr. Christakos returned my call.

Thanks to the doctor's quick response and our early intervention, my mother was able to be treated on an outpatient basis for this episode. My dad and I handled the household chores until she recovered enough to resume a normal level of activity.

It wasn't long before my father's eightieth birthday appeared on the calendar. At the time of his lung removal, the surgeon had said he could only guarantee that he'd be able to sit in a chair and breathe. Eighteen months later, climbing stairs and driving daily to the supermarket, he was surprising us all.

"I've been thinking about Dad's birthday," I told Ginny one day. "I think we should have a party. He's been doing so well." He was six months past his drop-dead date.

"Great idea," she said. "But I'm not sure he'll like it. You know how he hates to be the center of attention."

"Well, we'll make it so he's not. It's really just an excuse to get everyone together. I'll let you convince Dad to go. I'll hire a caterer and get invitations. Maybe we can ask Bill to put together a slide show of all our old pictures."

She agreed, sounding excited at the prospect of a party.

I rented a hall near my parents' home on a Sunday afternoon, knowing that their old friends would not want to drive at night. Later that weekend I mentioned our plans to Ron.

"Let me see if I have this straight," he said skeptically. "You're going to bring your father, who only has one lung, and your mother, who doesn't do well with crowds, into a banquet hall filled with people she won't remember, and have a party?" I smiled. This party was happening.

"You bet."

"In the middle of January?"

"Well, that's when his birthday is, isn't it?"

"And what if there's a blizzard?"

"We'll reschedule the party," I replied. "But we usually get blizzards in February."

"And what if your mother falls apart?"

"We'll have someone, maybe Bill, bring her home. The hall is only five minutes away."

"What if your father is having a bad day?"

"We'll have the party anyway, and tell him all about it."

Ron shook his head.

"Oh really, Ron, don't be such a killjoy. It'll be fun! January is a great time for a party; it's such a gloomy month. You just watch. Everyone will come." And everyone did.

On the day of the party, the forecasters predicted a winter storm. Luckily, it just rained. All morning Ron reported updates on the weather, graciously refusing to tell me he told me so. We arrived at the hall early and wondered how many of the old folks would stay home. The oldest couple among their friends was nearly eighty-seven years old, and while still able to drive alone, they lived more than an hour away. We didn't expect them to show, but they were the first to arrive.

"Unbelievable," Ron mumbled.

"Ron," I said delighted to see them, "you don't get it. This generation is made of tough stuff. They're only going to die when someone shoves them into a box and sits on the lid."

More than one hundred neighbors, relatives, and longtime friends arrived at the hall. Fifteen minutes into the cocktail hour, the entire over-seventy crowd was seated, awaiting the meal.

"Just like kids," I laughed, helping the caterer set out the food quickly. After dinner, we started telling stories about my father. Neighbors and friends recounted his antics during church suppers and road trips, along with his unsolicited and unwanted gardening advice.

One niece stood, winked at me, and launched into a humorous story about cribbage. My father taught each of his grandchildren to play the card game. And then, after they mastered the rules and their math facts, he'd proceed to cheat on them. When they inevitably caught onto his tricks, he'd feign surprise. "You're cheating, Grandpa!" they'd shriek in horror. "Am not," he'd reply. "Are too!" they would cry. "Am not!" he'd insist. I was often the one to serve as judge and jury.

"Yes, Grandpa cheats," I'd say. "Don't let him get away with it!" My father would then smile, having shattered their youthful sense of morality, and give his oft-repeated response: "Let this be a lesson to you. Never trust an old man!"

My brother Bill rose from the last table.

"My favorite story," he began, "was the time Dad decided to teach me something about accountability. I was four years old."

A wave of laughter echoed in the hall.

"I guess I had broken the basement window a few too many times, and after yet another pane was broken, he brought me to his workbench to help repair the damage. He made me sit on the grass next to the broken window as he carefully removed the shattered bits of glass. He cleared the edge of the frame of broken glass and measured each side carefully, writing down the dimensions on a slip of paper. With figures in hand, we drove to the hardware store, where I waited for the clerk to cut the glass to the proper size."

"After we returned home, I carefully put putty around the edge of the window frame and he inserted the new pane, gently tapping the edges into place with a small hammer. We found some Windex and a rag, and he made me clean the glass. It had seemed like an eternity, but the window was finally repaired."

"'See?' Dad had said wisely. 'That's how long it takes to fix a broken window. So, maybe next time, you'll be more careful.'"

Bill lowered his head theatrically, clasping his hands in front of his body, looking contrite.

"I nodded solemnly in agreement," he continued, bobbing his head so one could almost see Bill the little boy, ashamed and apologetic.

"Satisfied that I had learned my lesson, Dad began to gather his tools. 'So,' he asked casually, 'how did you break it, anyway?'"

"'Like this,' I replied, and I picked up the hammer and smashed the window again!"

The room exploded as everyone howled with laughter.

After dessert, my father stood near the door, saying goodbye to each of his friends, still laughing and joking as they opened their umbrellas and stepped into the freezing rain. My father's party was timely. Nine months later, he was gone.

NINE / Reflections on Grandpa

IN THE FIRST HOURS following my father's passing, I decided that our children, then ages eight and five, would not attend the wake or the funeral. It was an easy decision to make, for Ron and I both wanted the memories of their grandfather to be happy ones. But I also wanted to experience my father's wake as his daughter, not my children's mother. This was my time to grieve and I needed time. I needed time to recover from his death, time to reflect on my life with him, and time to fully appreciate his influence on my children.

During the five years since our return to Boston, Eric and Katie had seen their grandparents a few times each week. We celebrated holidays and birthdays together, cheered on the Red Sox from their living room couch, sat through Sunday dinners, and enjoyed the many small rituals that create an abundance of memories.

Dashing through the unlocked back door of their grandparents' home, Eric and Katie were often greeted by the delicious smell of their Nana's muffins baking in the oven.

"How's Nomar?" Dad would bellow, calling out the name of his favorite shortstop as he gave Eric a hug. Eric would most likely be wearing his Red Sox cap and favorite Red Sox shirt emblazoned with #5, a shirt I could only wash while he slept.

"Hey, Miss Kate, give me a smooch!" Dad would cry as she crawled up into his lap.

Katie and Eric knew their grandparents' home as only children do: they knew where the Playskool was stored; what cupboard held the chalk for the chalkboard; where the candy drawer was in the kitchen. They learned that grandparents have different rules about treats; my mother would insist that they make a goody bag before we left each visit. Eric and Katie would run gleefully to open the cabinet under the kitchen sink to find a plastic bag to fill with a few cookies, mints, or pieces of candy. They learned new uses for old words, too.

"Are you flush?" Dad had asked Eric one day, whose face assumed a puzzled expression, unsure about my father's inquiry regarding his bathroom habits.

"What, Grandpa?"

"Are you flush?" Dad had asked again, attempting to explain. "Do you have any loot?"

Still confused, I intervened. "Grandpa means, do you have any cash in your pocket?"

"No," Eric had replied innocently patting his pants. "I don't even have a pocket!"

"Muriel!" Dad had hooted in mock surprise. "Get the poor boy some cash! No grandchild of mine will be penniless!" And my mother, ever the supporting actress, scurried to find two dollars in her purse that Dad gave to Eric and Katie with a flourish, thereby establishing a weekly routine that continued for years.

"Mom," I had said once quietly in the kitchen, "You know I don't like the children to take money from you."

"Oh, Jan," she had cooed. "Don't make a fuss. It's no different than what we do for their cousins. Let Dad have his fun."

Over the months and years they spent together, my father did his part to instill his good humor in my children. He disobeyed "Nana's rules," winking mischievously after each scolding from my mother, creating gales of giggles. He snitched French fries from their lunch bags, negotiating playfully for more. He played endless games of cards, patiently moving their skills up the card-shark pyramid, from Go Fish, to gin rummy, to cribbage. He followed the Red Sox religiously, discussing the fine points of each game with Eric. Not surprisingly, Eric's passion for baseball was cemented by my father's companionship and although just a preschooler, Katie was not unaffected by my father's influence.

"Be a man," Katie said in response to my comment about how cute she looked in her poodle skirt as we skipped across a parking lot to a sock hop. "Grandpa told me to be a man."

"What did he mean by that?" I asked.

"He told me not to let anyone make me wear a dress or a skirt if I don't want to!" she replied petulantly, tugging on her skirt. I shook my head knowingly: another generation corrupted by his encouragement to think independently.

The children brought much joy and laughter to my parents' lives and they responded in kind, hiding their medical ailments from plain view. But the signs were everywhere if one chose to look for them.

My father had hoped that he would die in his own home, and as my last gift to him, I wanted to let him. While others may have marveled at his recovery, I knew better. I knew that he was living in constant pain, pain that was alleviated only on occasion by the Percocet he kept hidden in the top drawer of his bureau. He had stashed a bottle there after I had dumped an earlier prescription into the toilet in a pique, reminding him of his addiction to Serax. His Irish stubbornness and soldier's heart would not allow us to witness his pain, yet it was evident with frequent contact.

In the months following my father's party, my mother knew that his health was getting worse, and in her own way, she reflected how well, or poorly, they were faring each week. When their bills were neatly piled inside the desk cabinet awaiting my attention, they were having a good week. When the bills were missing, scattered around the house, or misfiled in the file cabinet, it was a bad week. When the casseroles or homemade soups that I left in the freezer had been eaten, it was a good week. When the food remained untouched, it was not.

My mother was like the canary in a mine: when she showed a sign of distress, my father's deteriorating health was the most likely cause. As the fall came around, she began to lose weight, a subtle signal that I needed to get more involved in my father's care. Ginny had noticed the change too, and expressed her concern at the christening party of their first great-grandchild that September. I had made a mental note to book an appointment, but three days later my father had called in desperation, looking for a ride to

Mount Auburn Hospital. It would be his last.

"Listen," I had told Ginny, "I don't know what's going on with Dad because I can't talk to the doctor with Mom staying with me. But I think you should make sure your daughters see him in the hospital."

"Is he that bad?" she had asked.

"I'm not sure," I had replied honestly. "But I think he was dying during that ride to the hospital. His cardiologist later told me that his pulmonary pressure was so high that the valves to his heart were not closing. Whatever is happening, the fun and games are over. Take the kids to see him while he's still able to be the grandfather they've always known."

Ginny made certain each of her daughters had visited their grandpa. We did the same with our children. During my visit with Katie and my mother, my dad seemed cheerful, uncomplaining, and upbeat. When our conversation lagged, he curled over a crossword puzzle with Katie beside him, who colored in one of her mini-notebooks with a washable marker. Ron and Eric had visited separately on Saturday evening. Like other visits in the past, it turned out to be quite a party, with several family members present.

Our conspiracy worked almost too well, for the family was stunned by my father's "sudden" death. In truth, I had anticipated a long, slow decline, but my father loved my mother too much to put her through that.

He died on a Thursday evening, before a long holiday weekend. That Friday morning I told the children and kept them home from school.

"No!" Eric had wailed. "I'm too young for him to die! Who am I going to talk to about baseball?"

"I want Grandpa!" Katie had cried aloud intermittently all day long as she remembered his passing.

"To be honest, I'm surprised that the kids are so upset about your father's death," Ron said that evening after they both were in bed asleep. "When my grandparents died, I wasn't all that broken up."

"Well, Ron, he was such an important part of their young lives," I said quietly, still in shock, too numb from the experience of having watched him die to say any more.

TEN / The Funeral

MY FAMILY IS BETTER AT planning parties than funerals, for despite eight years of warnings—throat cancer, bypass surgery, and lung cancer—we hadn't even begun to think about my father's funeral. The day after his passing, I met my mother and siblings at the Arthur Greene Funeral Parlor. My grandparents, family members, and most parishioners from their church were waked at Greene's. Arthur Greene and his wife had been family friends for more than sixty years.

A young man met us at the door of the funeral home and introduced himself soberly as Charles Greene. Some of us knew him as Chuckie. His young face and physiology seemed better suited for a polo shirt and tennis shorts than his gray suit and dark tie. I stifled the urge to laugh: he was taking his role quite seriously and out of respect for my mother, I played along. If my dad were alive, he would have broken the tension with easy banter. I just nodded solemnly and quietly thanked him for his condolences.

The funeral parlor was familiar, the dark décor unchanged from my first wake at age twelve, nearly thirty years before. The center hallway was flanked by two parlors, each with an alcove into which the casket was nestled for viewings. My grandparents had laid in the alcove, as had countless family friends and relatives. The memories of those past wakes engulfed me, and I was strangely comforted at the prospect of my father in these familiar surroundings.

Charles invited us into a back parlor. We scouted the room for six chairs and aligned them in front of his desk. He sat stiffly behind the desk and opened a folder. We were uncharacteristically quiet.

"Why don't we start with the details for the announcement in the newspaper," Charles suggested.

"Robert Albertson," he muttered as he wrote, "lived in Woburn, with his wife Muriel."

"Yes," I confirmed, wanting to spark a little amity into the conversation. "In fact, he graduated in 1937 from Woburn High School with your grandfather." Charles acknowledged the connection politely and returned to his notes.

"Did he attend college?" he continued, all business.

"No," I replied succinctly.

"Was he a veteran?" he asked. I stretched my neck to examine the length of his list of queries.

"Yes, he served in the Navy during World War II."

"Do you intend to have military honors?"

We looked at each other and at my mother, mumbling among ourselves. We hadn't even considered having a military funeral. He so rarely talked about the war; we never dwelled on his veteran status. After a round of gentle debate, we decided that a military funeral would seem ostentatious.

"He will have a flag, of course," Charles noted. "And just as an aside," he glanced my way, "if you can find his discharge papers, we can obtain a plaque for the gravesite free of charge from the government that will record his service history."

"Discharge papers?" I repeated, a bit incredulous, "from 1945?" He nodded as if everyone keeps fifty-year-old papers within arm's reach. I wrote a note to myself.

We continued down his checklist of items, reviewing my father's employment history, the names of his siblings and all children, properly spelled. We then discussed the wake and funeral plans. We were given the specifications for clothing and the protocol for holding the funeral service in the parlor instead of the church. That decision was based on our collectively unsaid but understood need to minimize the strain on my mother. Change brought on confusion.

"Was he a Mason?" Charles asked.

"Yes," I replied. "He belonged to the Arlington lodge."

"So, would you like a Masonic service?"

There was more family chatter and a consensus emerged that, yes, it would be nice. We did not want military honors, but a Masonic ceremony, dignified and subtle, suited his style.

"Where will he be buried?" Charles continued with his seemingly unending checklist.

"At the Puritan Lawn Cemetery in Lynnfield," I replied, wondering why funeral directors don't provide a family with an advance list of questions to expedite this meeting. His approach seemed highly inefficient and overly reliant on personal memory.

An uproar from my family interrupted my thoughts.

"No!" cried Walter. "He didn't want to be buried in Lynnfield. He's supposed to be buried with Granka."

"What?" I was confused.

"Dad told me that he was going to be buried with his parents, right here in Woburn," Walter insisted.

"Are you sure?" I asked.

"Definitely," he insisted. "Aunt Evelyn gave him Uncle Art's spot for Mom."

"And you're sure?"

"Yes," he said.

"He told me that too," Carol reported.

"Are you sure?" I sounded like a moron. And why didn't I know this? Two years of weekly visits, and it was never mentioned. In fact, their deed for the Puritan Lawn Cemetery was filed neatly in their file cabinet, in a blue folder labeled "Funeral Information." I shook my head.

"Well, then," I said to Charles, "It's Woodbrook Cemetery."

"I'll need a copy of the deed," Charles replied.

"The deed," I mumbled mindlessly, writing it down. *Of course you do*, I thought. *Let's see if I can find another forty-year-old document.*

Next, Charles pulled out a notebook with photographs of casket choices, neatly protected in plastic sleeves. It took every ounce of willpower to stop my eyes from rolling around in my head as Charles began his sales pitch of casket features and benefits by model and style. Knowing my mother's frugality, a pine box would do. I stayed out of that decision.

Despite our lack of preparation, the wake and funeral were

planned within ninety minutes. We left the funeral parlor together, my mother going with Ginny to sleep overnight at her house. Bill and I walked toward our cars that were parked along a side street in the opposite direction from the others.

"Bill," I said clasping his arm, looking around furtively to be sure that the others were out of earshot. "Can you believe that I would have buried Dad in the wrong place?"

"Yeah," he scanned for the others and began to laugh. I did too.

"Tell me," I continued. "How did I *not know* that Dad wanted to be buried with his father? Don't you think after two years of time together, every Friday, week in and week out, that it might have come up in conversation?"

"Beats me," he said, laughing louder.

"Can't you see it? All of us standing at the gravesite in Lynnfield, and Charles interjecting soberly, 'Excuse me, folks, it seems that we have a little problem here!'"

"How about Mom?" he added, fueling the fire.

"Oh my God!" I howled. "How could I tell her that we planted her husband in the wrong place?!" We were giddy with laughter.

"Oh my," I said, wiping the tears streaming down my face, "wouldn't Dad have loved this one!"

"He sure would," Bill replied, opening my car door and leaning on the frame. I kissed him goodbye and drove the two miles to my mother's house.

I unlocked the door and entered the house. Today it was quiet and still. Mumbling about the papers, I vaguely recalled seeing an envelope in the third drawer of their desk under a stack of old photographs and cards with a return address of Woodbrook Cemetery. To my delight, it was the cemetery deed, attached to which was a notarized slip of paper from my aunt. My grandfather had purchased the plot with six graves, one for each of his four sons. My aunt had given my mother her husband's space so that my parents could be buried together.

"Now for the discharge papers," I said aloud to the empty room.

I went upstairs to their file cabinet and pulled open the second drawer. There, in the back, I found the folder entitled "Navy." I flipped open the cover and was greeted by my father's young face in dress uniform. The folder included several photographs and papers and, sure enough, his discharge documents were tucked neatly in the back pocket. *Thank God for you Mom*, I thought, grateful for the time she had spent organizing their files. I found his clothes and placed them with the papers in my car.

I wandered through the house to tidy up for the funeral and walked out to the garage to clean up what remained from our summer project. That summer, Eric and I had visited my parents a few days each week to paint their garage doors. I collapsed into the folding chair that still stood where my father used to sit and supervise our work. Of course, on most days, I did the majority of the painting while Eric and Dad played raucous games of cribbage inside. On some days, Eric stayed in the house while my father and I chatted out near the garage about his father and his life as a boy. We had been looking forward to a school project that Eric would have that winter during which he needed to research one branch of his family tree. Now that project would never be done.

I stood up and folded up the chair. I returned the paint cans to their shelves and began to put the clean brushes away. My throat tightened and my stomach felt heavy. *This is too much to do today*, I thought. I had to leave.

I drove back to the funeral parlor to drop off his clothes, the deed, and the discharge papers, and then I headed home.

"How did it go?" Ron asked as I walked into the kitchen.

"It went fine," I replied. I briefly described the meeting, not wanting to review all of the details again. I was too tired and sad.

"What about contacting Chay, your father's brother, and your other aunts?"

"Ginny and Carol are taking care of that."

"Don't you think you should call them?"

"Ron," I sighed, "I've done enough for today. I'm done being in charge for a while."

"But you're sure that they'll call them?"

"I don't really care right now," I said. I left him standing in the kitchen and climbed the stairs slowly to our bedroom where I could be alone.

Late that night, restless and unable to sleep, I found a notepad and tried to write away the overwhelming sadness I felt. My thoughts wandered aimlessly across the paper.

Bring a suit, they said.

I unlocked the house door, moved past his favorite chair, near the paperback, opened flat to mark the page, and beside the remote control, an unfinished crossword puzzle. Climbed the stairs and in the closet I found his suit, the pants beneath a bit askew, no belt. How different from my husband's closet where many suits stand pressed in a row—he had only one.

And a shirt, they added.

I found several, white, unpressed, hanging limp from disuse. I chose the neatest, long sleeved. It's cold, a morning frost today. And a tie, dark blue, white dots, near the colorful ones, polyester, but I chose silk.

No shoes, they said.

I wanted to dress him as he liked: flannel shirt, brown pants, cardigan sweater. But not today: it's the suit, white shirt, silk tie, and eyeglasses, can't find the eyeglasses.

Choose a coffin, they said, metal or wood, silk or velvet, date of birth, survivors' names. Thirty percent deposit.

We're sorry, they said. We're sorry for your loss.

Sorry? Sorry for my loss? No one fully understood the impact that loss would have on my life over the next few years.

The Author's Guidance

In the first segment of *Don't Give Up on Me!*, you witness my parents' transition from what Mary Pipher, acclaimed author and psychotherapist, describes as the young-old to the old-old. This transition, one that is driven not by chronological age but by the extent to which chronic and debilitating diseases begin to impact independence, is an opportune time to take a few steps that will save you considerable heartache further down the road.

• Geography: Distance Matters

If you reside in Chicago, and your parents live in Florida, you may find yourself flying from crisis to crisis as they age. Take a moment to reflect on how you might move closer to them or have them move closer to you or to another family member.

• Legal Matters: What Matters

While most of us know about wills, the two most important legal documents that will help you more easily support your parents are a durable power of attorney and a health care proxy/power of attorney. Ask your parents to work with a lawyer to have these documents prepared while they are well. It is also time to talk about asset protection with a lawyer who specializes in elder law.

• Organize Key Documents

It may take a year or more to organize key documents into files and a safe deposit box, a good project for your parents to complete if they are able. Insurance, financial, and other records should be consolidated in one place, making it easy to find paperwork. Be sure to record contact information for their lawyer, tax accountant, and other key advisors.

• Medical and Mental Health

Depression, insomnia, and anxiety are not uncommon among elders, understandable as they deal with the loss of friends and family members and cope with the stress of seeking care for their medical ailments. If your family has not yet experienced mental health concerns, it is possible that you will do so with an elderly parent. In these early chapters, I recount incidents that highlight my mother's struggle with depression and the psychotic breaks that were caused by years of misdiagnosis and lack of treatment. It is my hope, as her story continues, that you will grow increasingly more comfortable with ways to best support your parents should they begin to show the symptoms of cognitive change. A caution: these symptoms may also be a side effect of prescribed medication.

• The Danger of Drugs

Do not underestimate the power of prescription drugs. They cure infection, dampen medical symptoms, and extend lives. If your parent, however, takes more than two or three drugs, he or she is at risk for side effects and adverse interactions. Dizziness, hallucinations, constipation, and what appears to be the start of dementia can be caused simply by taking the wrong drugs, at the wrong dosing, during the wrong time of day. Because elders may see several specialists who may not coordinate their prescribing habits, your parents may take ten or more prescriptions. Keep a list of medications, the dosing, and the time of day taken, and have their medication regimen assessed by a pharmacist and then by their primary care physician.

- **A Sense of Humor**

Your parents may be stubborn, childlike, and ornery. They may ignore your advice, refuse all help, and keep secrets about their well-being. They need your help anyway. Use laughter as a proxy for your own mental health. If you can't laugh, if you are losing your patience and perspective, you need to cultivate a network of friends and family to support you. Reach out for help.

The Transition

ELEVEN / A Test of Wills

MY FATHER'S DEATH meant an immediate change in our lives, for my mother could not stay alone for more than an hour or two at a time. Ginny offered to help care for Mom, and we agreed that we would take turns keeping her at our homes until we figured out what to do about a permanent living space.

I immediately set up the guest room in our house for my mother and created a list of tasks to tackle: her pension and health insurance, my father's life insurance, her medical appointments, and all that was required to ready her house to remain empty through the winter months. To my surprise, Ginny pressed to read my father's will while my brother Bill was in town. He had taken a two-week break from work for my father's funeral.

Read the will? It wasn't even on my to-do list. Most of my parent's assets were jointly held. By law, what my parents owned jointly now belonged to my mother. There was no need to read the will, no need, even, to go through probate. To me it seemed that simple, but after Ginny mentioned the will for a third time, I knew I needed to make it a priority.

The last revision of my father's will was written while my family lived in Princeton. At that time, my parents had called me to see if I would be the executrix of their estate. I declined, suggesting that it would be better to have an executor who lived near them or even co-executors, like Ginny with Bill or Walter with Bill. Although my oldest brother did not live in Massachusetts, his wife had been raised in Woburn and returned there often to visit family. I knew that my parents trusted Bill implicitly; my mother had nicknamed him "honest John" for his guileless demeanor and intelligence. We never spoke about the will again, but I knew a copy was in the files I took from my parents' home the day after my father died.

That Saturday, after several sleepless nights, I crawled into bed with the will and a copy of the power of attorney. I read the will first.

I, Robert A. Albertson, of Woburn, Middlesex County, Massachusetts, declare this to be my last will hereby revoking all wills heretofore made by me.

At this time, my heirs are my wife, Muriel M. Albertson, of said Woburn, my sons.... My father listed all five of his children.

First. I nominate and appoint my wife, said Muriel M. Albertson, to be the executrix of this will.

If she fails or ceases to serve as such, I nominate and appoint the following as co-successor executors in the order named: A. My son, said William A. Albertson and my daughter, said Virginia E. O'Neill. B. My daughter, said Jan L. Simpson.... He continued to list all of my siblings. *It is my desire that there always be two executors of this will upon the failure or cessation of my said wife to act as executor.*

The phrase "failure or cessation of my said wife to act as executor" caught my eye but I continued reading.

Second. Except for my said wife, each executor who serves as such during the probate of this will shall be entitled to receive a fee for such service equivalent to 5 percent of the net worth of my estate in addition to any share to which such executor may otherwise be entitled to hereunder.

Wow. So according to the will, if my mother failed to act as the executor, Bill and Ginny would become co-executors, each receiving 5 percent of his net worth for their trouble. His net worth included not only his savings, but also the value of their house and the contents. It didn't seem right. That would be a lot of money for my mother to give away at this point in her life, when she would likely need every dime for her future care. My eyes narrowed and I kept reading.

Third. I give and devise all my property and appoint all property over which I may have power of appointment to my wife, said Muriel M. Albertson, if she survives me by ninety (90) days.

So, as long as my mother served as the executrix and lived for three months, she would get all of the property cleanly. The will went on to describe how to handle the estate if my mother did not survive beyond ninety days.

I sat back on the pillows and reflected upon the will's contents. My mother was clearly intended to be the sole recipient of my father's assets; the caveat was my mother's ability to serve as executrix. Her age, mental illness, and status as a forgetful, grieving widow could be used to challenge her capacity to fill that role. If Ginny and Bill became executors of my father's estate, my mother could lose 10 percent of her net worth unless they declined to accept that fee.

I rubbed my forehead absently. I did not want to start down this path. My parents and their lawyer had tried to anticipate problems by assigning me as the power of attorney. Was there anything in that document that would help? I pulled out the paperwork. It began with the usual legalese.

Know all men by these present that I, Muriel M. Albertson, of Woburn, Massachusetts, do hereby constitute and appoint my daughter, Jan L. Simpson, of Concord, Massachusetts, on any occasion or occasions as she may see fit, to be my true and lawful attorney for me and in my name and stead.

Unlike a simple power of attorney document that might be found at a bank, my parents' lawyer had listed nineteen specific activities that I could engage in on her behalf, including renewing or paying debts; opening any safe-deposit box; endorsing checks; managing, maintaining, or selling all real estate; filing tax returns; establishing trusts; making health care expenditures; and representing her before the IRS. The list was lengthy and inclusive. I kept reading.

My attorney, Jan Simpson, shall have, in complete and uncontrolled discretion, the possession, care, management, and control of all my affairs, personal and otherwise, my property, both real and personal, wherever situated and of whatever nature... to do and transact all business and other matters of any and every kind and nature, and in every place, to execute any and all documents and instruments, for me and in my name or behalf as fully as I might or could do if I were present.

There it was. The phrase, *"to execute any and all documents for me in my name or behalf,"* meant that I could legally execute my father's will on my mother's behalf, literally as if I were standing in her place before the court. There was no need for any of the others to get involved. No need for them to see her savings, to appraise her house, or to get any part of her money until my mother herself was gone.

I was momentarily thrilled, delighted to be able to sidestep any discussion about wills and assets. But a nagging doubt surfaced. What about guardianship? I skipped over the rest of the document and my eye caught paragraph C.

In the event that a petition is filed in any Court for the appointment of a Guardian or a Conservator for me or my property and estate, I nominate my daughter, Jan L. Simpson.

My eyes stung and a tear rolled along my cheekbone. They had thought of everything.

The first time I had seen this durable power of attorney, I hadn't understood the fine details. At the time, I was just amazed that my father was so willing to let me handle their money. I had anticipated my mother's initial resistance to my paying of their bills, and frankly, I wondered if I could give one of my children that much control. Yet I now understood the importance of his decision. By turning to me two years ago, I had time, a few hours each week, to learn how they managed their household. I knew where their money was invested, where the insurance policies were stored, how their pension was distributed, and where their tax accountant lived. I might not have known where my father wanted to be buried, but everything else was under control. It would take only a few months to transition all of the paperwork seamlessly.

After reading both documents together, I now understood something else, a subtlety I had never before considered. By embedding guardianship in the durable power of attorney, my parents signaled clearly that they wanted me to retain control of their financial well-being until they had both passed away. Of course, a court hearing would be required if I needed to legally become my mother's guardian, but by embedding their wishes into the power of attorney, my parents had made it unnecessary, unless one of my siblings insisted on becoming my mother's guardian, to go through the time and expense of a court case.

Later that morning, I made a copy of the will and the durable power of attorney and brought them to Ginny's house when I went to get Mom.

"Ginny," I said, "I know that you want to go over the will. I don't really have time to do that right now, but I want you to see what it says." I spread the documents across the kitchen table.

"Dad's will says that Mom is the executrix and its sole beneficiary."

"Yes," Ginny interrupted, "But really, Jan, you don't think she can handle this, do you?"

"Well, actually, I do," I said. "She is still able to make decisions and I can handle the paperwork." Ginny pursed her lips and shook her head slightly.

"Look, Ginny," I continued before she could say more. "Dad and Mom set things up so that I could handle their finances until both of them died. Here is a copy of the power of attorney. No one has ever seen this, but it's pretty detailed. I'll leave this copy for you to review." I pointed to one section on the page. "You see, I can act as Mom's agent and execute the will without her, if necessary. That's what this means. Of course, I won't do that, but I will put the paperwork together and then have her do the rest. That's how things were set up."

Ginny nodded silently and we never talked about my father's will again.

TWELVE / Living with Nana

IT HAD BEEN MORE THAN A MONTH since my mother had spent a full day at her house. That Monday, she and I dropped my children off at school and drove to her home with lunch, my list of chores, and plans to pick up the children midafternoon. I unlocked the door, turned on the teapot, and placed our lunch in the refrigerator. My mother circulated from room to room, raising the shades to half-height, adjusting a doily here, a magazine there, showing a simple joy at being in her own home surrounded by her own possessions. She reminded me of my daughter Katie who, upon returning home from a weekend away, would wander around our family room, touching all of her belongings, each stuffed animal, block, and puzzle piece, as if reclaiming her place in the universe. My mother's gestures were equally innocent: she was re-anchoring herself in her old world, the world in which she had spent so much of her life, as a wife and a mother and a grandmother.

As I watched her, I knew that she was unaware of just how much her universe had changed and would be changing with my father gone. I knew something that she did not, and I couldn't bear to tell her. She would never be moving home again.

I wanted an excuse to leave her alone in her home, so I walked over to the neighbor's to retrieve her mail that had been accumulating for weeks.

"Oh, Jan," her neighbor Marjorie cried, "I feel so awful. I am going to miss your father so much." I always marveled at how much emotional support others seem to need when it's you who has lost a loved one.

"I know Marjorie, I know."

"I keep looking over at your mother's house, hoping to see her shades up. Every morning for more than forty years I've opened my blinds in the den and looked across at her windows to see the shades raised, knowing that they were already awake and having breakfast. It's been so sad to look over and see the shades down."

"Well," I sighed, forcing a smile, really just wanting to collect the mail and go home, "The shades are up today."

I thanked her for her help in watching the house and returned to my mother's home, finding her upstairs puttering around in the bedrooms. I left her alone and placed a few telephone calls to cancel the cable service and arrange for a fall cleanup of the yard. I wandered downstairs to the playroom, and then into the laundry room where I found the floor under the washing machine flooded.

"Damn it," I whispered, scouting for the source of the leak. I found the leaky valve, covered the floor with paper towels, and went upstairs to call a plumber.

My father's plumber was Charlie Black; I had graduated from high school with one of his sons. I called the Blacks, explained my father's passing, that I only had a few hours with my mother at her house, and asked to have someone sent out urgently. I returned to the basement and began mopping up the mess, carrying the portable telephone with me. Shortly thereafter, it rang.

"Hi, this is Charlie calling." An unfamiliar voice echoed over the receiver. "Is this Jan?"

"Yes, and thanks for calling so quickly," I said, unrolling a length of paper towels onto the wet floor. I watched the water soak into the paper.

"I'm sorry about your Dad," he replied sympathetically. "I just read about his death in the newspaper. I didn't know that he was sick."

"Well, he had been ill for a while," I said, bending over to place the soggy paper towels in a plastic bag.

"What was wrong?"

"He had been battling cancer for a long while, but he died quite suddenly," I said, putting another layer of paper towels on the wet floor.

"How's your mother doing?"

"As well as can be expected," I said patiently, but I was becoming anxious to get off the phone. I checked my watch.

"Well gee," he continued, clearly unaware of my growing impatience, "I wish I had known about the funeral. Some of the boys and I would have wanted to attend."

Attend the funeral? Is he trying to make me feel guilty that he didn't know about the funeral? My patience snapped and I stomped on the soggy paper towels. *Unbelievable! Here my father dies, and the first thing I'm supposed to do is call his plumber?*

I nearly missed his next remarks.

"On Friday?" I mumbled catching the end of his comments. "You talked to my father on the Friday before he died?"

Now I was really confused. My father's last weekend alive, and he called his plumber? My mind raced back to that last weekend. Charlie? My father called Charlie?

"Oh my God," I said into the receiver. "Uncle Chay, is this you?"

"Yeah," he said. "I feel so bad about not knowing that your dad died."

I am going to kill Ginny and Carol.

This was Chay, my father's oldest and only remaining brother: eighty-seven years young, with a memory like my father's, the physiology of a sixty-year-old man, and an incredible musical talent, able to play any song, religious or ragtime, on the piano upon request. I knew him only from his childhood nickname. Chay. Charles. Charlie.

"Oh, Uncle Chay," I tried to explain. "I thought you were..." *the plumber? Never mind.*

We chatted for a while and I made plans to bring my mother over for a visit soon, hoping in a small way to compensate for the fact that no one had reached him about my father's death. While we were chatting, the doorbell rang, and in came the plumber to repair the leaky valve. By the time we had eaten our lunch, the leak was repaired and I had completed my checklist of chores. Looking out the kitchen window, I noticed Pete Stanton walking by, and I went outside to say hello. Pete lived in the house behind my parents and had known me since birth. I filled him in on my mother's plans to stay with us and asked him to keep an eye on her place.

As we were chatting, my mother opened the back door.

"I'm here, Mom," I said, "just talking with Pete. Why don't you finish up what you're doing so we can get ready to pick up my children from school?"

"Your children?" she replied backing away from the doorway. "I'm not leaving until your father gets home!"

I froze on the sidewalk and then glanced quickly at Pete. He stared silently at my mother.

"Okay," I said. "I'll be in shortly."

She shut the door, and I retrieved the mail from the mailbox.

"It's always nice to see you, Pete," I said, glancing briefly into his eyes. I didn't know what else to say. "Thanks for watching the house."

"Good luck, kid," he replied, patting my arm for support.

"Thanks," I said, smiling meekly. "I think I'm going to need it." I turned and walked back to the house.

My mother stayed with us for nearly two weeks, shifting to Ginny's house to give me a break. That night, over dinner, I thanked the children for their kindness in welcoming Nana into our home.

"Why does Nana follow you around?" Katie asked with a child's natural curiosity.

"Well," I said, drawing out the vowel to buy thinking time, "Our house is kind of big and she's not comfortable in it yet."

"But she follows you *everywhere*," Katie persisted.

"Yeah," Eric added. "It's kind of weird."

They needed a better answer. I didn't want them thinking that their grandmother was weird, but my mother's behavior was hard to ignore. If I went upstairs to make the beds, she trailed along; if I went out for the mail, she joined me; if I opened the garage door to recycle the newspapers, she nearly raced across the kitchen to stand by my side. I encouraged her to relax; I tried reminding her where I was going each time I left the room and how quickly I'd be back. I even began singing "Me and My Shadow" as she followed me from room to room. Nothing worked. It was weird, but how do you explain dementia to a five-year-old child?

"Nana is afraid of being alone," I started, and Katie's eyes widened.

"Why?" she whispered, no doubt surprised to learn that adults have fears too.

"Well," I said gently, "Nana and Grandpa were together every day for twenty-five years after Grandpa retired. Nana was never alone. Then one day, Grandpa was gone, and now Nana is worried."

"Worried?" Katie asked as Eric stared silently.

"Yes. She's worried that when I leave her alone, even for a few minutes, that I won't be back too."

"But that's stupid!" Eric offered, shaking his head. "You are just going to get the mail."

"I know it seems stupid." I was not giving up. I would not let them think ill of their grandmother.

"Do you remember when you were little?" I said to Katie, all of five years old. "Do you remember in preschool how there was a classroom window that looked into the hallway?

"Yes," she said.

"Do you remember how I would stand in the hallway and wave goodbye each morning?"

"Yes," she nodded.

"Do you remember, sometimes, having a funny feeling in your tummy that maybe, just maybe, I was leaving you and I might not come back?"

"Yes," Katie nodded, her brown eyes widening with her realization.

"That's a bit how Nana feels right now," I said. They grew silent, and I knew they now both understood.

We agreed to be patient with Nana, to give her time to get used to living with us. The next time Nana came back to stay, the children simply smiled when she followed me around. Katie even offered once or twice to stay with her as I went upstairs to finish some chores. We slowly adjusted to having her with us seven days a week, but it was wearying. On the weekends, Ron helped out by running the kids to their games and lessons. But during the week, when Ron was away, I still needed time alone with the kids and time for myself. If this was going to work, my mother had to fit more smoothly into our daily routine.

I started with the mornings. For the first few weeks, I had been waking her early, cajoling her to eat and dress before joining me to drive the children to school. One day, I tried an experiment, setting out her cereal bowl, banana, morning medications, and a teacup with a note saying that I'd be back by nine o'clock. When I returned, she was awake, enjoying breakfast in her nightgown and robe, seemingly content to awaken at her own leisurely pace. Suddenly I had one hour alone. Evenings were another problem, for Eric and Katie both had long bedtime routines that included reading and quiet conversation. It was our time set aside each day for each other, but my mother wouldn't leave us alone. Asking for time alone with the children, assigning the evening dishes to load into the dishwasher, even locking the bedroom doors did not stop her repetitive interruptions. One evening, I tried a new routine.

"Mom, I'm going to put the children to bed now," I said, usually the signal for dozens of interruptions. "Why don't you get ready for bed yourself?" I knew that it took her more than an hour to do whatever she did in the bathroom to prepare for bed.

"After the children are asleep," I said winking, "I'll make some tea for us, and we'll have the rest of the night to spend time together." She loved the idea, and I got back my evening routine.

Not everything, however, went over smoothly.

"You yelled at Nana today," Katie said glaring at me over dinner one night. My mother was away for another stay with Ginny.

"No I didn't," I said defensively.

"Yes you did!" Katie repeated. "Nana was only asking where to put the spoons!"

For the fiftieth time, I thought.

"I didn't yell at her," I said, but I was sensing a losing battle.

"Yes you did," Eric chimed in.

"That wasn't nice," Katie insisted, pursing her lips at the injustice. "It's not nice to yell at Nana."

Great, I thought. *It's bad enough I have to put up with my mother when she's here. Now, when she's gone, I have to face the inquisition.* Looking at Katie's face, I knew my evasive tactics were not going to work.

"You're right," I said. "It wasn't nice, and I'm sorry."

She continued to stare, unconvinced by my apology.

"Okay, okay," I sighed, "I said I'm sorry. Nana kept interrupting me when I was trying to help Eric with his homework."

"You didn't have to yell," she persisted. *Oh, this is pathetic. Trying to elicit forgiveness from a self-righteous five-year-old child?* Our debate was exasperating, but I felt a small twinge of pride; beneath my pitiful protests, I was grateful for Katie's feelings of protection and care.

"You're right," I said. "I'll apologize to Nana the next time she comes over."

"Good," Katie replied, satisfied that I appeared sufficiently contrite.

I needed a new routine for my mother in the late afternoon. After school, Eric liked to study on the island in the kitchen. I typically prepared dinner while he worked, available for the occasional question or to chat about his work. My mother insisted on joining us, repeatedly interrupting our conversations. I tried involving her in preparing supper or emptying the dishwasher, but that only led to dozens of questions, constant chatter, and sometimes chaos. I needed to get her out of the kitchen. But what do you do to amuse an elderly woman with no short-term memory? I went to the library.

I brought home a large-print book written by humorist Erma Bombeck. *If she doesn't read this,* I thought, *I will. God knows I could use a good laugh.*

That afternoon, I fixed a pot of tea, placed a soft pillow in a cozy leather chair, found an afghan to cover her lap, and encouraged my mother to sit in our family room and read a bit while Eric studied and I prepared dinner. To my surprise, she settled in contentedly. I had found our new routine.

I ordered large-print versions of *Guideposts* and the *Daily Word*, with short articles that might encourage her to keep reading. I ordered subscriptions, despite knowing that one copy of each would last the year, as she read, then re-read, then re-read again, the same story without recall or familiarity. It was worth the price for my sanity.

*   *   *

One evening at bedtime, I sat on the edge of Eric's bed and ran my fingers through his sandy brown hair as we talked about his day, the soccer game at recess, the latest antics of his friends, a new computer game. He paused for a moment and then looked up at me with big eyes, black and glittering in the darkness of his room.

"Mom," he said, "I don't want to hurt your feelings, but, uh…" I smiled slightly in the dark. He always saved some of his most pressing questions for our before-bed chat.

"What is it, honey? You can't hurt my feelings."

"Well, don't you sometimes wish that it was Nana, instead of Grandpa, who died?"

He said it quietly, turning his head away from me toward the window to stare outside at his favorite tree. The second he asked the question, my fingers froze in his hair. The simple honesty of his question had caught me off-guard and I wasn't quite prepared to respond. I was grateful for the darkness that masked the expression on my face.

"No," I said slowly. "I don't wish that Nana had died."

"Grandpa was so much fun," Eric continued," "But it's different now. Why did he have to die?"

I shared with Eric more details about my father's medical issues, details about which he had been unaware. I was glad to elicit Eric's feelings about my father's death: his grieving had been largely unspoken, though profound. He had suffered the loss silently, weeping during hymns in church, but avoided all talk of my father until bedtime. He didn't wish my mother dead, of course, he was just unable to grasp why Nana lived and Grandpa did not.

Later that evening I returned to the kitchen, cleaning up the supper dishes. As I stacked plates into the dishwasher, I reflected on Eric's question. How did I feel about my mother? It was a question I had largely avoided. But our relationship was profoundly different than my relationship with my father.

I loved my mother, of course, and respected the fact that she had raised five kids with little money or support. Yet I often joked with Ginny that we had stayed in school because our mother was the role model for the life we didn't want.

My mother's universe began at the mailbox and ended at the backyard hedges. When I was young, she arose well before dawn to prepare breakfast, do the dishes, and pack lunches for my father and the five of us. She washed five or six loads of laundry daily, carrying the basket of wet clothing up the basement stairs to the clothesline in our backyard: back and forth, up and down, over and over again until the last sock was dry and the last sheets were windblown. Every morning after cleaning both bathrooms and washing the kitchen floor, muddy from our feet the night before, she would bake and cook, turning leftovers into casseroles or bits of meat from roasted chicken into soup. After school, I would find her standing over the ironing board, pressing my father's and brothers' white shirts, ironing our dresses and skirts. Supper was served promptly at half past five, so my father could eat between the end of one job, working on the docks or in the machine shop, and his second job. When he returned later that evening around midnight, she was still working, mending our clothes or crocheting an afghan, still awake so she could serve him tea and a snack before bed. She did it all and rarely complained.

As I grew up, we grew apart. She clipped coupons and cleaned closets; I worked on weapons systems with hazardous materials. I traveled for work, venturing to places I could only afford to read about as a child; she found bargains at the local grocery store. She seemed puzzled by my ambition. When I graduated from business school, she told me that she hoped I would take time out for myself. She meant that she wanted me to get married, as if my degree was a task I had to complete, like picking up milk at the grocery store, but of no real significance to my life. To her, marriage and children were not only the most important things in life, they were the only things that made life worthwhile.

My mother was delighted when I returned to Boston with our children, misreading that change as a sign that I was ready to

LIVING WITH NANA 91

give up my work and raise my family near her. My father knew otherwise. He knew that the change was likely to be temporary, one made to provide our children with the blessings of an extended family and a childhood spent in the safety and beauty of a small New England town.

It was now two years since I had stopped consulting. I had planned to resume work that fall; indeed, I had to cancel a business dinner the evening that I rushed my father to the hospital. Now that he was gone and my mother was living with me, I faced another delay in returning to work; it would take time to settle her financial affairs and establish an appropriate living arrangement. Two years away from my business network, even three, would certainly be of little consequence, but I could not afford to stop working for much longer than that. I recognized that the strain of juggling my mother's needs and my children's activities would be challenging, but there was an end in sight. There had to be.

I can do anything for a year, I thought, turning on the dishwasher.

I am thankful that I did not know then all that lay ahead.

THIRTEEN / We Need More Space!

SPACE. Lack of space, not enough space, cramped for space, too little space. Each conversation with Ginny focused on the same topic: space. While Ginny had told everyone at our father's wake that my mother would be living with her permanently, the reality of housing three teenagers and one five-year-old daughter, two dogs, a ferret, two working parents, and an elderly woman was growing intolerable.

"You said that you would help me," she complained one morning on the telephone. "Lindsey has given up her bedroom and is now sleeping on the couch. Mom wanders into my tutoring sessions and constantly interrupts me. This isn't going to work Jan, not without more space."

She was right. While my mother adjusted slowly to new routines in my house, she adapted poorly to the bustling chaos of Ginny's home. She nagged the girls to sit up straight, fussed over the natural clutter of teenagers' rooms, interrupted Ginny's tutoring sessions repeatedly, and seemed unappreciative of all attempts to make her feel welcome. If my mother's presence was the problem, more space was the answer.

I should have been more understanding, but Ginny's complaints annoyed me. I wanted to remind her that our father had been dead for only six weeks, and that I kept my mother for as many consecutive days as possible, before exhaustion forced me into bringing her to their house for a break. Understandably, she had no sympathy for me: I had ample space, two children, and no work pressure. And while I did have serious doubts about having my mother live with Ginny, Ginny thought that the issue was settled. No one in the family challenged her intentions, but each of my siblings had approached me, quietly hinting that it might be unrealistic to allow my mother to live with her family. On paper, Ginny and Jon were the most qualified to care for our mother since they both have experience in mental health. But realistically, they had full-time jobs and four children, with little free time for themselves, let alone time to care for my mother. It wouldn't work: there had to be a better choice.

I needed more time: time to grieve, time to finish up paperwork, time to think about what would be the best living arrangement for my mother. My father had said to keep her in her own home, to bring in home care. My oldest siblings made no offer to help with her care. Ginny would take her in, but my mother seemed, at least for the moment, most comfortable with me in my home and I wasn't sure what to do. I wanted to evaluate her options thoughtfully, to create the best environment to care for her until the end. I wanted time to think.

"We need to talk about your mother," Ron said a few days later, after the children were asleep and we were watching television in the den. Ron's tone of voice indicated that this would be a difficult conversation. My stomach sank. *No, not yet,* I thought, *my father has only been gone for a few weeks.* "You know that I love your mother and that we will do whatever is needed to take care of her." I nodded silently, waiting for his "but."

"But she cannot live with us permanently," he said. I held my face expressionless.

"Why not?" I asked weakly, unable to say more.

"Look, Jan, I'm worried about you. If I were home during the week, if it were just you and me, it would be fine. She could stay here. But you cannot do this alone; you cannot ignore how she affects you." Ron reminded me of my hospitalization from a panic attack a week before my father died, as I began to feel the end of his life approaching, aware that he would soon leave my mother behind with no definite plan for her care.

"You think that you should do this—you think you should keep your mother with us," he continued building his case. "But I know what it takes to care for someone who is chronically ill. Your mother has five children—five, not one. Let the others help. I will not let you work yourself into an early grave. Think about our kids."

I nodded silently, stifling tears and frustration, and picked up a book and pretended to read. I had thought that Ron was too preoccupied with travel and work to realize what was happening at home. Things were worse with me than he had thought, and the fact that I didn't push back, that I didn't insist that he was wrong, was a major red flag to him. After reading a few pages without absorbing a word, I went to bed early.

I awoke at three o'clock in the morning, slipping silently downstairs for a cup of tea. This was becoming my evening, or early morning, routine, one that had begun the night my father died. There was no sense in lying awake in bed until dawn. I made a pot of tea, sat on the couch in the den reading a magazine, hoping to fill my head with words and images that would lure me back to sleep.

Following my father's death, I felt myself standing alone at the bottom of a deep, deep well of sadness. Every morning, I dragged myself slowly upwards toward the light at ground level, moved numbly through my daily routine, and returned back to my well at night, to the cold comfort of my darkened space. My husband's words only deepened this well. As I sipped my tea, I felt a twinge of anger that quickly dissolved: I was so tired.

I could taste the loss of my father. He was more than a parent or a jovial soul mate, he had been my most steadfast supporter, uniquely qualified to advise me in rather unorthodox ways about my life and career.

"Jan," he had said one day, "I spent the first half of my life angry. I'd fight anyone on a dime. It took years before I got it through my thick Irish head that you get further in life if you try to get along with others. Now, you have an Irish temperament, and you have to choose how to handle it. You can be stupid like me, and fight everyone or every wrong you see, or you can smile, kill them with kindness, and walk away. It will drive the bastards crazy." I tried to laugh at the memory of these words, but my eyes welled with tears.

Reaching for a tissue, I looked slowly around the room trying to regain my composure. We had built our home to accommodate all four grandparents: indeed, the den I was sitting in was a first-floor bedroom, complete with a handicapped bathroom. Ron's words had caught me off-guard. I had begun to think that my mother might live with us permanently; at least I wanted that choice. I shook my head, nuzzled deeper into my well, and thought about my mother.

Although I did not feel as close to her as I had to my father, my mother's influence on me was no less significant. A natural teacher, she had encouraged my early reading and math literacy through games, songs, and activities. She recognized every milestone, birthday, and holiday with family parties, celebrations, and barbecues. She was clever, teaching me to knit, sew, crochet, and embroider, and showing, by example, that with a bit of imagination and a pinch of time, we could make most of what we needed. With scraps of fabric, she made a cradle from a Quaker Oats container for my first baby doll, created flowers from napkins as the candy-holder favors for my tenth birthday party, and kept a stash of handmade gifts that she gave to friends and others to acknowledge their help or to celebrate a special occasion in their lives. As a result, I never envied others who had more material wealth than my family. I had all that I needed and more than I wanted.

The back door of my parents' house was always unlocked for the friends and family who dropped by for tea and conversation. Whenever they did, she stopped working, brought out whatever pastry she had baked that morning, and chatted unhurriedly at the kitchen table, always ready to listen to whatever reason brought someone to her door. Her social life centered around the church, and I fell asleep many nights during my teen years listening to the cackling laughter of the women's guild seated at our dining room table, filling baskets for shut-in elders or planning the next church supper or craft fair. On Sundays, my mother frequently invited young soldiers stationed at a nearby Air Force base to join us for dinner, knowing they might enjoy a home-cooked meal and the banter of a large family.

I sipped my tea, thinking about Ron's words and my father's

wishes. My mother did have five children, but I knew that it would likely be only Ginny and me who would actively care for her. My father had left it up to me to decide what was best for my mother. My mother would not have a choice in the matter: she was not able to make that choice. It was up to me, and it was time for a plan.

A week later, I called the architect who designed our house and arranged for a meeting with Ginny and Jon.

"You're not seriously thinking about having your mother live there, are you?" Ron asked when I told him my plans.

"I don't know where she's going to end up," I replied. "But the design fees will be worth the price of keeping Ginny off my back until I get through the holidays."

That was only a partial truth. Ron was right to be concerned about my health. That panic attack was an early warning signal of my inability to handle the stress of my mother's care. He was right to question my actions, for Ginny and Jon were not going to be able to properly care for my mother without more space and tremendous help from us. But in the few weeks since my father's passing, it was obvious that my mother was gravely ill, living with a terminal disease that would soon require active caregiving. She would not likely be a candidate for assisted living, even if I had time to research that choice, but would need special care in a skilled nursing facility. If Ginny and Jon were her only option to stay out of a nursing home, then I would do whatever it took to make her comfortable there. Ron was right to question my judgment, but he underestimated my resolve. My mother would only be placed in institutional care over my dead body.

FOURTEEN / My Siblings

B Y THANKSGIVING, my oldest three siblings had decided how much daily support they were able to give our mother: little to none. Bill had raised the issue after taking our mother for a weekend so I could bring my children to see Ron's parents in New York City, alluding to some family issues that would make it difficult for Mom to move in with them even temporarily. My sister Carol, who already had her eighty-seven-year-old mother-in-law living with her, considered adding an extension to her house for both old ladies, but had decided—wisely, I would admit—that she wasn't cut out to run a nursing home. And Walter?

"Walter is in California," Ginny mentioned one day on the telephone.

"Oh, that's nice," I said without interest.

"Yes, apparently he's still quite upset about Dad's death, so Judy thought they needed a vacation."

"I see." I turned and looked out the window at the dreary November rain.

"I think we should let him take Mom for a week or two," Ginny said mischievously. "After a few days, he'll forget all about Dad. He'll be too busy to grieve."

"No kidding," I laughed, grateful that Ginny did not acknowledge what we both knew was the underlying reason for Walter's grief: he blamed me for our father's death.

Thanksgiving that year was a sorry affair: only Ron, the kids, and I were there to share dinner with my mother.

"I'm surprised that no one wanted to spend time with your mom on her first Thanksgiving without Dad," Ron observed as he carved the turkey in the kitchen. "It's just as well," I replied, stirring the gravy on the kitchen stove. "To be honest, I couldn't stand being with any of them right now, and it would be hard for me to hold my tongue."

Our mind-numbing routines continued through December, as my mother grew increasingly more comfortable in our home. She helped with dishes and folded laundry, attended hockey practices and gymnastic lessons, and read quietly while the children finished their homework. We all grew accustomed to her presence and quirky habits, like her insistence on carrying her purse around the house, from the family room to the kitchen, from the kitchen to the laundry room, afraid that "someone might take it."

"Mom," I said one day, hoping to break the habit, "you can leave your purse on the chair if you want. We're all alone in the house."

"Oh?" She raised her eyebrows, eyeing me suspiciously. "You never know who might want to get into my things!"

Over time I learned to choose my battles wisely, ignoring her sudden attraction to a crocheted hat trimmed with angora, which she insisted on wearing in the house from morning until bedtime. In our house, the abnormal was becoming normal.

My mother appeared to be, for the time being at least, living life in the present tense, enjoying the rain and sunshine, outings and books, a warm dinner and a hug at bedtime. In fact, after two months of repeatedly running her back to her old house, thinking it was healthy for her to spend time in her own space, I observed that she seemed happier and more content to simply stay with us. I decided to limit the visits to my parents' house, where memories evoked by her home often made her confused and disoriented. She continued to remember my father—after all, it's hard to forget spending fifty-nine years with someone—but she had forgotten that he had died. Only once did I make the mistake of reminding her.

One night, as I went into her room to say goodnight, I found my mother sobbing in bed. Evenings are often the most difficult time for people with dementia: like young children, the darkness conjures scary thoughts and turns shadows into ghosts. I walked to her bed and sat down on the edge, resting my hand lightly on her shoulder.

"Mom, what's wrong?" I asked gently, rubbing her back. "It's okay, honey, there's nothing to be afraid of." She turned and looked up at me with big wet eyes.

"Your father, Jan. It's your father. He hasn't been coming home, and he hasn't called either." She winced. "Jan, I think there's someone else. There must be another woman, why else wouldn't your father come home or, at least, call me?" She burst into tears again.

I was heartbroken, second-guessing my decision to allow her fading memory to erase her husband's death.

"Oh, Mom," I said sadly, "Dad didn't run off with someone else. He hasn't come home because he can't come home. He died."

She stared up at me for a long moment, a small, short gasp interrupting her tears. She shrieked, and then began to wail, louder and louder until I worried she'd awaken and frighten the children, asleep across the hall.

"Dead?" she wailed. "He's dead? Oh, no, no, no. He can't be dead! How am I ever going to care for all of these children?"

It was my turn to gasp. Children? What children? I was her youngest child; she had no children to care for any longer. In my mother's mind's eye, though, she was now a young widow, laden with the burden of raising five children without a father. It took me an hour to calm her down.

*   *   *

We spent Christmas in New York City with Ron's family and, as penance, spent New Year's Eve babysitting my mother. Ron and I made the best of it, renewing an old family tradition by cooking lobsters, a delicacy we could only afford once a year as children. The tradition signaled hope for a new year of prosperity. I hoped for sanity.

Eric and Katie had never cooked lobsters before, and Ron's antics made certain it would be a memorable night. Eric shouted with glee as a lobster attempted to back out of the pot of boiling water, while my mother, dressed in her nightgown and robe, helped Katie decorate a banner. After all were in bed, Ron and I opened a small bottle of champagne in the kitchen.

"Well," Ron said cheerfully, "Your mother certainly had a good night."

"Yes," I said wistfully, a lone tear rolling out the edge of my eye. "She always loved a party. I wish my father had lived to see this new millennium. Three months," I whispered as Ron reached out gently to wipe the tear away, "he only needed to hold on for three more months."

That night I pushed the demons back into their cage, hopeful that the new year would somehow bring an end to the endless nights of interrupted sleep and unwelcome grief.

The new year brought the finished plans for my mother's addition to Ginny's house. At the start, I had recommended that they include a bedroom and bath for my mother, as well as an extra bathroom for Ginny's family in an attempt to keep her daughters from considering my mother's space as their own. Foolishly, I had told Ginny that Ron and I would cover any overage until my mother's house could be sold. The final plans shocked me. They included a bedroom, two bathrooms, a living room, dining room and kitchen, a two-car garage, and two storage areas. It seemed like a lot of room for a woman who couldn't drive or cook. I suggested that Ginny revise the plans since they exceeded our budget. She refused and reminded me of my commitment to cover the overage.

I was outraged. Legally I was responsible for carefully managing my mother's money and would not waste it on space she did not need. I organized a family luncheon, hoping the others would put Ginny in check.

We met at a local restaurant in Woburn, the site of many earlier family celebratory dinners. While my siblings poured over the menu, Ginny pulled me aside and showed me a change she was making to the construction plans, moving a wall that would separate my mother's place from hers. I stared wordlessly at the plans and then into my sister's eyes as my stomach sank and a wave of nausea spread from head to toe. Before the permits were filed, before the foundation had been poured, Ginny was already planning to use some of my mother's space. I sat at the table and reached for the water goblet, too nauseated to comment or complain. *This was a mistake.*

I had intended to start our family discussion with a joke, but it fell flat. After much chatter about children and jobs, we circled around to a conversation about Mom.

"She belongs in a nursing home," Carol said, and my brothers quickly agreed.

"But Carol, I don't think she's ready for a nursing home, and Ginny doesn't either," I said weakly, "yet we do need to do something about her space."

With that as her cue, Ginny passed the plans around the table. I attempted to draw their attention to the unnecessary space, the size of the project, and the impact on their inheritance. No one seemed to understand.

"What will you do with Dad's things?" Carol asked. "Jessica would love to have his cribbage board."

"I took his tools," Walter said and invited Bill to come over that weekend to sift through them to see which ones he wanted.

"There's nothing I really want for myself," Carol continued, oblivious to my silence. "Well, except maybe one thing. I'd love to have Nana's rocking chair."

I couldn't believe what I was hearing. I needed to get away from all of them.

I asked for the check and paid the bill in full, just to get out of there quickly. Ginny approached me briefly as I unlocked my car door, but the pounding in my head was louder than whatever she was saying. Waves of nausea rolled over me as beads of sweat trickled along my forehead. *This was a mistake.*

I could barely see well enough to drive home; my car found its way a mile from the restaurant to the cemetery where my father was buried.

I crawled out of the car, stumbled to the gravestone, and slumped against it, sobbing. The ugly truth of my mother's situation had finally hit home. Although she was physically able, capable of climbing stairs and managing her own dressing and hygiene, she needed a full-time companion, help with food preparation, and transportation to doctors' appointments. The only alternative to a nursing home was for her to live with Ginny. But this luncheon, the construction plans, and the conversation about her belongings made me question my initial instinct that my mother was better off living with one of her children. I felt so sorry for my mother. I had failed her. I wept uncontrollably.

The worst part of this experience was that the only person I knew who could advise me in how to straighten out this mess was lying six feet below. I sobbed relentlessly. *I am so weak,* I cried. *This is too much. I can't do it.*

A voice startled me into silence. *You have the money.* I looked around to see who had spoken. I was alone.

I have the money, I repeated mindlessly and I leaned back against the headstone, taking deep, ragged breaths, rubbing my face, streaked with tears, on my shirt. *I have the money*, I repeated again.

Slowly, I calmed down and began to think. Until that moment, I had never considered my parents money as my money. They had saved well and were cautious about spending; it was not my place to challenge their decisions.

I have the money.

I thought about what I would do differently if I considered my mother's money as my own. Certainly, I would make some changes. My husband and I knew little about caring for elders, but we knew much about making and managing money. I pulled myself together and stood slowly, staring down at my father's grave.

"How did it go?" Ron asked when I arrived home.

"Well," I said, "What would you like to hear about, how Ginny is planning to use some of Mom's space, or how everyone wants to divide up her stuff?"

"That good, eh?" he replied, as I walked straight past him into my office. "What are you doing?"

"I am going to take care of my mother," I said fiercely, and I pulled open my desk file. I looked over the spreadsheets listing all of my mother's assets and began to sketch out a plan of action to bolster

my mother's income. I was buying my mother time: time to spend
at basketball games and gymnastics meets with her grandchildren;
time to attend the christenings of her great grandchildren; time to
enjoy the colors of spring, the heat of summer, the autumn leaves.
I would give that to her. "Use the money for her care," my dad had
advised, "all of it."

That's just what I was going to do.

FIFTEEN / Nana's Infectious Disease

AFTER MY MELTDOWN at the cemetery, I added one more item to my list of tasks: self-preservation. I called Ginny and told her to proceed with the addition of space for our mother, reminding her of the budget, and I discussed the construction plans with my brother-in-law, the contractor, giving him an upper limit for costs. I then reserved a small condominium in a quiet corner of northern New Hampshire for eight weeks during July and August. I was not going to spend my summer debating sink prices or window choices. Despite missing my support for our mother, I was sure that Ginny would prefer to supervise construction during those summer months without my presence.

It was March, Katie and Eric had a two-week spring break, and unlike in the past, we made no plans for a vacation. To my surprise, Ginny offered to take my mother for the first week, prompting Ron to suggest that we spend a few family days in Washington, D.C. We visited the White House and the Smithsonian, laughed at the antics of the Harlem Globetrotters, and connected with some old friends whose son was in remission following aggressive treatment for childhood leukemia. Over dinner with our friends, I gazed at the healthy glow on their young boy's angelic face, reminding me that my troubles were insignificant. That Saturday, Ron checked our home answering machine for telephone messages.

"You need to call Ginny," he said apologetically, no doubt sorry that he had decided to call home.

"Why?" I asked, unable to hide the annoyance in my voice. "We'll be home on Monday morning. It can't wait?"

"There's a problem with your mother," Ron said. "The battery on her pacemaker died, and Ginny scheduled one-day surgery for Tuesday. She wants to make sure that you can take Mom."

I spent all day Tuesday at the hospital, supervising my mother in the recovery room, bringing her home for a light dinner and an early bedtime. The next morning she awoke feverish. "She must have a post-op infection," I said to Ron, mumbling about the genius of same-day surgery for elderly people. "I'm bringing her back." I contacted Dr. Harmon who recommended admission through the emergency room, and I spent a second full day at the hospital, leaving her after supper. That Friday, anticipating her release, I arrived at the hospital, surprised to find Dr. Harmon at her bedside. "She has an intestinal infection," he said. He explained that that this infection, common among elderly people, was causing diarrhea and that he wanted to keep her in the hospital over the weekend to get the diarrhea under control. I readily agreed.

That Monday, back at the hospital, I bumped into Dr. Harmon on his early rounds. Tests had confirmed his suspicion that my mother was infected with *Clostridium difficile*, or *C. difficile*. He mentioned that he had consulted with an infectious disease specialist for treatment.

"Infectious disease?" I parroted. "So, does that mean that we're all going to catch this?"

"Oh, no no," he said comfortingly. "Healthy adults have strong immune systems that routinely fight off bacteria. This infection only impacts the elderly and young children, or adults with immunocompromised systems, like AIDS patients or patients undergoing chemotherapy."

"So, if I give her a separate bathroom to use, and bleach it thoroughly, we should be all right?" I asked, knowing that she was not going home to Ginny's house with its one bathroom.

"Yes, and I can arrange for a nurse to explain to you how to care for her." Dr. Harmon stepped away from the hospital bed, preparing to leave and continue his rounds. This was a bit too much. He was intending to release my mother, still suffering from bouts of diarrhea, into my care with nominal instruction from a busy nurse?

"That would be nice, Dr. Harmon," I said, trying to hide my sarcasm, "and I will also look into hiring a visiting nurse to come to our house until she is well." I paused as he headed for the door. "You mentioned that this infection affects old people and young children. Do you consider my five-year-old daughter to be a young child?" The anger in my voice blocked his path. He turned around to face me, and I reminded him that my mother now lived with young children in a household that routinely had infants and toddlers visiting.

"Don't misunderstand me," I said bluntly. "I want my mother to come home with me. I just need a couple of days to set things up so she doesn't give this to my children or any of their friends." He nodded and left me alone with my mother to visit.

That evening I called Carol, knowing that a friend of hers worked as a visiting nurse. Carol arranged for nursing coverage, but the first available slot was on Thursday. It was only Monday. Tuesday morning, the hospital's discharge nurse called and said my mother would be released immediately that afternoon as soon as Dr. Harmon signed her discharge papers. Apparently, though, he wasn't answering his page.

"They're going to release her tomorrow," I told Carol later that afternoon. "How long can Dr. Harmon keep avoiding the nurses?" We both laughed, shaking our heads in disbelief. "Carol, how pathetic is our health care system that a doctor is reduced to playing games to provide the best quality care for his patient? I really don't mind bringing Mom back home, but the problem is, I honestly don't know how to care for her. She has an infectious disease, not a bad cold. I don't know what to do."

"Tell them you can't take her home until Thursday," Carol replied, displaying the feistiness that someone like me, who always plays by the rules, secretly admires. "They would have to find her a bed, probably in a nursing home, but that would take a day of paperwork and by then, she'd be home."

I smiled at her cleverness and followed through with our plan, brushing off the angry reaction of the discharge nurse. "I can bring her home on Thursday," I told the nurse repeatedly, until, exasperated by my refusal to pick up Mom, she conceded, barking, "Be here first thing in the morning!"

The visiting nurse arrived on Thursday with a box of items, including plastic gloves and a plastic spray bottle for bleach. We arranged for coverage from 7:00 a.m. through 9:00 p.m., when my day with the children typically ended. I felt momentarily guilty about spending my mother's money for a week's worth of nursing care, but I wanted her supervised by experienced help. I would take the night shift, 9:00 p.m. through 7:00 a.m. The nurses showed me what to do, how to clean my mother, shower her if necessary, and clean the bathroom each time she used it. I had hoped that she would sleep through the night on her first day home, but one hour after the children fell asleep, I heard her in the bathroom.

Drawing a long breath before opening the bathroom door, I turned the handle and entered, catching the expression on my face in the mirror above the sink. When I signed on to help my parents, I had established a few internal parameters, one of which was that I would never provide them with physical care. I would pay their bills, intercede with the doctors, take care of their house, provide them with food, and deal with my siblings, but I would not clean them or shower them, wipe their bottoms or wash their hair. Ginny didn't seem bothered by that prospect, but I found it extremely disturbing. Nudity? No thanks. I would hire a small army to avoid any task that included physical care. How trivial was my earlier concern. Here was watery diarrhea and deer-in-the-headlights confusion in my mother's eyes. Sleep deprivation, Depends adjustable underwear, bleach, rubber gloves: this-is-your-life. Think you have control? Forget it.

I cleaned her up, tucked her into bed, and spent the next hour bleaching the bathroom. She awoke two hours later.

Dr. Harmon had mentioned that some elders develop a chronic case of this *C. difficile* infection, often referred to as simply *C. diff*. After her first episode ended, she went to stay with Ginny for a week, only to return with another wave of *C. diff*. A second trip to the doctor's office, and a third to a local emergency room, confirmed what we suspected: she had developed a chronic case of the disease.

Coincidentally, the father of one of Eric's friends is a physician, a former head of the western Centers for Disease Control, and one of America's experts on infectious disease. His wife volunteered his help and arranged for me to contact him. Naturally, I was mortified. Who was I to talk about one old lady's diarrhea with one of our country's leading experts, a man currently developing vaccines for smallpox, West Nile virus, and other scourges of the world? I tried reminding myself that feces and disgusting biological fluids that would stimulate a gag reflex in most people are somehow intriguing to physicians and researchers in his field of expertise. I swallowed my pride and placed a call to his cell phone.

"Tom," I began, "I appreciate your taking time to provide advice."

"My pleasure," he replied, and I raised my eyebrows and grinned. *Oh, I'm sure.*

"*Clostridium difficile*," he told me, "is a common bacterium found in nursing homes and hospitals that unfortunately preys on the elderly."

"It's common?" I repeated, surprised that I had never heard of it before. Tom assured me that it was a common infection, so prevalent in nursing homes that he and other colleagues were developing a vaccine. My mind lingered on that word: vaccine. I knew from my experience in the pharmaceutical industry that vaccines, with their low profit margins, are developed only if the potential market is enormous. This infection was not simply common, it was widespread.

"My mother isn't in a nursing home though," I said, "so how did she get it?" I explained the defunct pacemaker, her one-day surgery, and her return to the hospital with a postoperative infection.

"The antibiotics that were administered to her in the emergency room lowered her resistance to infection," he said, launching into a discussion of how the *C. difficile* bacteria infect a person. "Our intestines are full of bacteria," he said, "some good and some bad." My mind envisioned a grassy, open field, with soldiers aligned on opposite sides for hand-to-hand combat. The good bacteria, like that found in yogurt, routinely surround and destroy toxins that invade our body. C. *difficile*, a bacterium that is shed in feces, lies dormant in the air in a spore, where, like a guerilla fighter, it awaits the opportunity to attack. Nursing homes, hospitals, and even day care centers, where the staff routinely deals with fecal matter, are loaded with C. *difficile* spores. Antibiotics, given to kill bacteria, do not discriminate between good and bad bacteria: every soldier is wiped out. In healthy adults, reinforcements are quickly assembled to protect the host, but in old people, children, or adults with weak immune systems, the reinforcements are sluggishly assembled, allowing the C. *difficile* to multiply rapidly, overrunning the battlefield. Diarrhea is the body's way to rid itself of bacteria before the infection spreads to vital organs. Flagyl, or other medicines that stop diarrhea, can actually cause more damage, allowing the C. *difficile* to remain longer in the colon and multiply. My head was spinning.

Then Tom mentioned the most damning information. Antibiotic-associated C. *difficile* is one of the most common infections acquired by patients while they are in the hospital. After a stay of only two days in the hospital, 10 percent of the patients will develop infection with C. *difficile*. In fact, more than three million C. *difficile* infections occur in hospitals annually. This was unbelievable.

"Tom, if I can understand the problems associated with giving antibiotics to old people in a hospital environment after a five-minute conversation with you, and I am not a health care professional, shouldn't the nurses or doctors have known better?" He offered to connect me with a colleague, Dr. Fadia, who was running a clinical trial with the new vaccine. Perhaps my mother could participate in that trial. I thanked him and hung up the telephone, so stunned that I could only sink slowly into a chair at the kitchen table.

I'm not sure what bothered me most: the sudden realization that elders don't die of old age, but of infection caused in part because of their own susceptibility to something like C. *difficile*, or my own naïveté in thinking the best recourse for my mother was to return her to the hospital for care. How different might her recovery have been had I simply called for a prescription for antibiotics and kept her at home? I refused to linger any longer on the thought. I am not a physician, I told myself, and her fever could have been caused by any number of issues. I was not the problem here.

Early the next morning, I called Dr. Fadia's office, expecting to talk with his nurse to set up a time for a telephone appointment. Dr. Fadia answered his own telephone and interrupted his morning duties to talk with me. Because of her dementia, my mother was not, in fact, eligible to participate in the clinical trial. To my surprise, however, I was relieved, perhaps because I didn't want the responsibility of subjecting her to a study with an unclear outcome. I had enough to worry about. Instead, Dr. Fadia recommended a treatment protocol that might rid my mother of the infection. The antibiotic my mother took, called vancomycin, successfully wiped out the *C. difficile* bacteria and stopped the diarrhea. Apparently, though, with prolonged vancomycin use, the *C. difficile* bacteria smarten up and mutate into new strains resistant to attack, like body armor on a battle-worn soldier. So, why not substitute another antibiotic and keep destroying the enemy? It turns out that vancomycin was the antibiotic of last resort: at the time, there were no stronger antibiotics on the market. Once resistant to vancomycin, my mother would simply die from infection. Dr. Fadia recommended a war game, using a low dose of vancomycin in concert with yogurt and a pill called acidophilus. By slowly cutting back on the number of vancomycin tablets taken over several weeks, my mother could potentially win the war and rid herself of this scourge. It was worth a try.

I wrote out a two-page schedule that listed my mother's pills each day, making it easy for Ginny to follow. We decided to try this approach over the summer, when Ginny's work schedule was more relaxed and my mother was permanently stationed in one place.

It was May, and the warmth of spring buoyed everyone's spirits after the longest of winters. Despite her ongoing struggle with infection, my mother's gentle disposition remained intact, easily following the routines we had established in the fall. Construction had begun on her new apartment, and I found myself counting the weeks until I could escape north to New Hampshire. Before I left, though, I wanted to put her house up for sale. I called three realtors, Walter contacted a fourth, and we got a range of potential sale prices with a $40,000 difference between the lowest and highest price. After interviewing each realtor, I selected a middle-aged woman who wanted to list the house near the top of the range and seemed less inclined than the others to drop the price to make a quick sale. She, too, had cared for her own elderly mother and understood that even a few extra thousand dollars could mean the difference between home care and a nursing home at the end of my mother's life.

The house was in excellent repair and meticulously maintained, but it did have the somewhat tired appearance typical of the home of two elders. I called Walter's wife, Judy, who has a flair for decorating, and asked her to stop by for an hour on Saturday to get ideas on how to quickly spruce up the place. She arrived at the house like a breath of fresh air, clothed in bright colors and large jewelry, her blond hair perfectly cut and her nails recently manicured. She whisked from room to room, nodding her head, making mental notes.

"I'd like to change the wallpaper," she said, eyeing the orange-flowered paper in the dining room, "but we don't have time. And what's under this rug?" Her foot tapped the brown wall-to-wall carpet installed thirty years before.

"Hardwood floors," I replied and her eyes sparkled.

"Great! I'll have Walter rip up the rug and have the wood refinished next week."

To my surprise, Judy stayed to help me pack boxes. While we worked, she called Walter about the floors and arranged for her nephews to stop by the following day to move some furniture. Later, I confided in her about the guilt I felt in leaving my mother at Ginny's house. Judy dismissed my concerns airily, noting that my mother would be fine.

"But Judy," I said sadly, "she really wants to live with me." I knew that my mother would be better off if Ginny and I shared the responsibility for her care but I still felt the enormous weight of guilt, a pervasive feeling that I was letting my mother down by placing her in a bustling railroad station with people coming and going at all hours of the day, instead of the quiet sanctuary of my home. Judy laughed.

"Of course she wants to live with you!" Her voice grew louder and more buoyant. "Who wouldn't, Jan? You have a beautiful home, two great kids, and you and Ron are a lot of fun. We ALL want to live with you!" She burst into laughter. Judy refused to let me wallow in guilt.

"Jan," she said seriously when she saw that her words had had their intended effect, "You do enough."

Enough. Good enough. Those words were just not part of my inner compass. I never did anything just good enough and Judy understood. We were women with similar characteristics. When we saw a need, we filled it. When we faced a problem, we solved it. We didn't sit around and whine about our troubles. We jumped in, feet first, and made things happen.

My mother was standing in an ocean of need. I could not just wait on the shore and watch the angry ocean waves buffet her frail body with their icy touch. I was compelled to jump into the surf and hold her steady, to keep her from going under. Each wave, however, brought a new challenge. No sooner was one challenge addressed, than another wave of trouble arose, and then another, and another. There was no end in sight, no solution. All of my accumulated experience, all of my energy, could not stop the waves from battering her, could not stop the deadly undertow from pulling her fragile body farther and farther from shore. I could only hope to support her with a human chain of help that could keep her tethered to shore. I needed rest. I needed to accept that good enough was indeed enough, and more than sufficient. For beneath these waves, the hands of death were slowly extending their bony fingers, encircling my mother's ankles, waiting for the right moment to snap her under and drag her away. I was learning to let go and not a moment too soon, for events were about to take a turn for the worse.

SIXTEEN / Psychiatric Admission

FOUR WEEKS REMAINED until our summer trip to New Hampshire. I could taste the mountain air, anticipate the chill of ice cream on my tongue, and envision long, leisurely days spent playing, reading, or swimming with Eric, Katie, and Ron. Construction was underway on my mother's apartment and while we didn't yet have her *C. difficile* under control, we had a plan. It felt good to know that what was likely one of the worst years of my life was nearing an end.

To be honest, I felt guilty about leaving my mother behind for the summer. I certainly needed a break for my own mental health but I needed something else, too. My summer away would be a chance to see if Ginny and Jon could handle my mother living with them permanently. Before I sold my mother's house, before I resumed work in the fall, I wanted to see how my mother would fare if I were not always available on call. I told my older siblings about my plans, asked them to help out, to call if there was trouble. I was, after all, only three hours away.

Just before our summer break, we went to New York for a weekend to visit Ron's parents. As I read in the sunroom of his parent's house, Ron came in looking worried.

"You need to check the messages at home."

"Why?" I asked, lowering the morning newspaper. "Can't you just tell me what they say?"

"You need to listen to the messages."

I stood and grumpily sipped the last drop of my morning coffee before wandering into the kitchen toward the telephone on the wall. As I punched in our home number, I didn't notice Ron quietly rounding up the children and sending them upstairs to

113

their grandparents. I stared wordlessly at the microwave as two messages from Ginny played back in my ear.

"McLean?" I said aloud. "She put her in McLean?" I turned toward Ron, now leaning against the frame of the kitchen door. "I don't believe this!" I barked, slamming the telephone onto its receiver. Ginny had admitted my mother to McLean Hospital, a psychiatric hospital in Belmont, Massachusetts. Ron stood silently.

"Well, Jan," he said quietly, "It's not a total surprise, is it? You've been expecting your mother to crash."

"In October, yes, when my father first died, but not now, nine months later!" A bolt of anger shot through my body. I stomped into a bedroom and began tossing clothes into Eric's duffle bag.

"Tell me, Ron, how does my mother go from emptying my dishwasher one day to admission to a psychiatric hospital four days later?"

Ron's face softened with empathy. "Do you want to leave now?" he asked.

"No!" I replied angrily. "We came here to visit with your parents. The kids won't be seeing them for a couple of months. Let's have breakfast with them, and then we'll leave afterwards."

It was late afternoon when we arrived home and I left immediately for the hospital. As I drove along the highway, I felt a growing sense of dread at the thought of my mother committed to a mental institution. I preferred that she be treated in the psychiatric ward of a medical hospital—it seemed more normal. Psychopaths and serial killers went to mental institutions, not forgetful old women. I turned off the highway, winding my way through a residential area, past the fairways of a tony country club, and up a steep hill toward the McLean facility. The hospital was in an odd location, like a place from the *Twilight Zone*. One minute, I was traveling along a country lane, stopping at a lone stop light with no intersection; the next, my car was winding slowly onto the hospital grounds. The hair stood up on the back of my neck.

My mother was staying in the first building, an administrative building with two floors used for older patients. The parking lot was adjacent to the building, so I didn't have to drive much farther into the campus. I was grateful: I did not know what bogeymen lay waiting for me beyond the hedges. It was growing dark and the grounds were eerily empty.

I parked the car and walked warily across the lot toward a side entrance. With each step I felt my body tighten, like a soldier entering a combat zone. My eyes searched all corners of the building, watchful for any unusual movement. My heartbeat quickened, my lungs expanded, and my mind increasingly focused on my physical movement. I did not know how I would find my mother; I didn't know what shape she might be in; I did not know if this was the end. I willed myself to cut off all thought and emotion. I was there, my mother was ahead somewhere in that building, and, for the time being, I shut down all thoughts beyond getting to her side. No matter what I saw, no matter what I felt, I would do whatever it took to see her.

I walked past a small brick patio with an empty bench for absent smokers. I pulled open a heavy door and stepped onto a black rubber mat in a dimly lit entrance. On my right was a window, like a ticket booth in an old cinema. I stepped up to the ticket window half-hoping to see a pink-cloaked silver-haired volunteer stationed to dispense room numbers as in normal hospitals. But this was not a normal hospital. My eyes met the security guard's back, who was turned, talking quietly to another guard. I studied the patch on her sleeve as I waited for her to acknowledge my presence.

"I'm here to see Muriel Albertson," I said in a slow, steady voice. "She's in AB-2. I'm her daughter."

"Go through the door, turn right, and head down the hall to the elevator," the guard said dismissively. "There's a phone on the wall with the numbers to call. Call the floor and they'll let you up."

I nodded, tugged on the inner door, and stepped into a dimly lit hallway. I stood for a moment in the doorway, staring blankly at a red brick wall. Turning right as directed, I glanced quickly over my shoulder, but the hallway faded into a darkened blur. I walked past an empty office, the wooden door and bubbled glass reminiscent of my ancient high school, and continued stealthily along the corridor to the bulletin board at the end. Two steps to the left of the board, the hallway opened into a dead end with a single elevator bank and a telephone above which, posted on yellowed paper, were two sets of faded four-digit numbers. I punched in the numbers for AB-2 and waited.

"Yes?"

"I'm here to, uh, see my mother, Muriel Albertson, who was admitted last evening," I said into the phone. "I'm her daughter, Jan."

"Okay." The line was disconnected.

Now what? I thought. I moved cautiously toward the elevator and pressed the up button. The doors opened and I entered. I stood there, waiting, but nothing happened. I pressed the button for the second floor. The elevator doors closed, but the elevator did not move. In a moment, the doors reopened and I stood facing the beige telephone. I waited inside the elevator, indecisively, as the seconds ticked by. The doors closed abruptly and the elevator began to move upward.

Suspecting that the halls and elevators were monitored, I stood still, my face emotionless, my jaw clenched. I had been on locked floors in medical hospitals where the doors in and out of the psychiatric wing were locked and could only be opened by an attending nurse. This was my first experience with a locked elevator. I felt anxious.

When the elevator doors opened, I stepped out cautiously. An aide, holding the elevator key, stood waiting nearby for the doors to close. She told me my mother's room number and I started off in the direction she indicated. I walked through the dayroom, long and narrow, lined with a misfit collection of vinyl chairs with silver legs. The placement of the chairs against the wall gave the patients full view of visitors walking along the hallway. An ancient television set droned at the end of the room, ignored by two old women dressed in housecoats who stared blankly at me. An old man slept hunched in a wheelchair. *Thank God she has a private room.*

I breathed, in and out, and slowly made my way toward my mother's room. I heard a hoarse whine, continuous, rhythmic, like a cat, or a child long ignored, who cries not for help but for solace.

The door, left slightly ajar, dampened the sound but the whine persisted, grating and lingering like fingernails across a clean blackboard. I glanced quickly at the room number. It wasn't hers.

Across the hall, I entered my mother's room. She was lying on the plastic mattress of an unmade hospital bed, without any sheets or a blanket, pushed against a window with the curtain closed. The room was freezing and my mother, wearing only a thin hospital gown, lay shivering on the mattress, curled up in a fetal position. I stepped around a cardboard box and moved toward her bed and noticed the clothes she had worn to the hospital tossed across the only chair in the room. She had been wearing what looked like an oversized pair of my brother-in-law's navy sweatpants, covered with dog hairs. I suppressed a spark of anger. A food tray at the foot of the bed held two pieces of dried pressed turkey, shriveled potatoes, and serrated carrots; the food, like the room, was cold. My gaze returned to my mother, still shivering in a drug-induced sleep. I glanced at her legs and noticed that she was wearing a diaper filled with feces.

Thank God you won't remember this, I thought. *And thank God I will.* I opened the drawers of a small nightstand and found a clean diaper. I checked the closet for her blue suitcase to see if there were any other items of clothing with her but the closet was empty. I turned to leave the room to retrieve some clean sheets from a linen cart I had seen in the hallway, and I noticed that the cardboard box near the door, which was large enough to hold a television set, was filled nearly to the top with putrid diapers. I paused, staring at the contents, thankful that severe allergies have reduced my sense of smell. I retrieved a blanket and sheets from the linen cart in the hallway and returned to my mother's side.

"Mom," I said, with my face close to hers. "Hi, honey, it's Jan."

She opened her eyes and smiled up at me weakly.

"Mom," I said, "I've been in New York. Ginny brought you here to the hospital for a checkup. I'm going to make up your bed in a minute, but I need to clean you up first. Can you get up and come into the bathroom with me?"

"Okay," she said sleepily.

I helped her get out of bed and I guided her to the bathroom. She sat on the toilet while I searched for items to clean her: the bathroom had only toilet paper and brown paper towels. *This is great*, I thought, shaking my head. *My mother has an infectious disease and there's no soap, no bleach, and no gloves.*

I got her out of her diaper and, using only water and paper towels, cleaned her up as best I could. I changed her diaper and dressed her in two hospital gowns along with her sweater. I sat her gently on the chair and, while I made up the bed, I tried to explain to her where she was.

"You're in the hospital," I told her, allowing her to believe we were in Mount Auburn Hospital if she wanted. "I haven't talked to the doctors yet, but I will tomorrow. You won't be here long."

"Okay," she replied sweetly.

"I know that you're tired, Mom," I continued chatting, as I helped her back into bed. "I want you to sleep as much as you can while you're here, okay?" I would rather have her asleep than alert and aware of her surroundings.

"Okay," she said, snuggling under her blanket.

"I have to go home now to get the kids to bed," I continued before she fell asleep. "But I'll be here tomorrow morning. I promise." I gave her a kiss. "Get a goodnight's sleep Mom. I'll see you tomorrow."

"Okay," she said dreamily. My chest tightened, my head felt full. I had to get out of there.

The hoarse screams of her neighbor followed me up the hallway to the nurses' station. I found an aide and asked if my mother was admitted with a suitcase. The aide said she hadn't seen one. I told her I was leaving and she brought the key to unlock the elevator. I rode down quickly and walked silently toward my car.

I arrived home as Ron was putting the kids to bed.

"How is she?" he asked.

"You don't want to know," I replied. "Let's get the kids to bed."

It was more than an hour before I could give Ron the briefest of reports. We agreed to talk further in the morning.

While Ron prepared for bed, I grabbed my pillow and a blanket and stretched out on the couch in our den. There was no point in having us both lose a night's sleep. Slowly, I let my mind drift back to the scene I had witnessed in the hospital, trying to process my feelings after seeing my mother, lying in a diarrhea-filled diaper, shivering on a cold mattress alone in a hospital room.

How could anyone do that to her?

I had promised my father that I would take care of my mother, no matter what, until the end. He had always been fearful that she would end up in a psychiatric hospital, abandoned and alone, and I had just walked in on his most feared nightmare. Tears rolled down my cheeks as I stared out the window of the den into the purple night.

How could Ginny leave Mom like that? Poorly dressed, suffering from uncontrollable diarrhea, rambling—no wonder she was neglected by the hospital's medical staff. They likely thought she had come from a nursing home with no family to watch over her.

I rolled over and tried to fall asleep, but tonight, sleep would not come. I couldn't stop thinking about my mother: shivering on a bare mattress, drugged beyond comprehension, scraps of cold food on that cold tray, the stench of the box filled with putrid diapers.

My tears subsided as I searched for the cause. Certainly, we were a good family who wanted to do right by my mother. We fed her; we filled her days with activity, grandchildren, sunshine, and hugs; we took her to the doctor and met her every need. *How did she end up in that place?*

I wanted to blame Ginny for bringing her to McLean, but was that the real problem? Ginny was doing her best. She was exhausted, too. *It's not fair,* I thought. *Ginny and I have the least amount of time, our children are young, but the oldest three do so little. What's the matter with them? Can't they see what's going to happen to Mom if we don't help her? Can't they see what's happening?*

This was different from my father's illnesses. Sure, he was left alone in the hospital. But his mind was sharp and his sense of humor connected him to his doctors, nurses, and aides. My mother was vulnerable. She couldn't express her needs. She was mentally ill, and the medications they gave her made her a zombie.

That night, I dozed fitfully, awoke repeatedly, revisiting the scene, searching for answers. I finally allowed myself to see the obvious, to comprehend what caregivers of chronically ill children or adults know all too well. This was not the case of one overworked health aide or poor medical practices. My mother was the victim of a virus pervasive in American society, one that threatened to end her life prematurely. The virus is particularly insidious because it does not infect the elderly person, but the people around them. It hides behind the professional demeanor of the young intern, it masks itself in the smiling embrace of adult children, it sneers at token gestures of love and gratitude. The virus has a name: it is called indifference.

Indifference. My mother was a dying, old woman. Did it matter if her life ended prematurely because of poor nutrition? Or bedsores? Or an infectious disease? Or improper medication? Who cares? She was already dying.

The scene in the hospital was a glimpse into my mother's future: neglected, unwashed, unfed. That image filled my brain with a liquid poison that spilled over and flowed through my veins. My faced burned, my arms tingled, my back ached. I felt an emotion I had never before experienced, a sensation so violent that its intensity frightened me. I tried to suppress its fury, but to no avail. It filled my body repeatedly, spilling its venom until my body shook and trembled. This emotion was rage, pure unbridled rage.

The injustice of my mother's treatment overwhelmed me. She had done nothing to deserve such disrespect and humiliation. She had made countless personal sacrifices to raise the five of us, to see that we were well fed and well educated. She had cheered our successes quietly, loved our children, and provided a welcome refuge to all who stopped by for tea and conversation. She could not control this disease, which was slowly destroying her memory and her physical strength. My body shook with rage as I tried to absorb the shock of what was happening. I could not and I would not stand by and watch it happen.

In the early morning dawn, I declared a jihad on the medical system and any person who stood between my mother and her ability to live well and die with dignity. I closed my eyes, shook my head sadly, and said a short prayer for strength. Sleepily, I raised my body from the couch.

"By God, Mom," I said quietly, as I stretched my aching limbs, "they will never do this to you again."

SEVENTEEN / Summer Escape

I GOT THE CHILDREN OFF TO SCHOOL the next day and quickly gathered items to bring to the hospital: latex gloves, soap, paper towels, and a spray bottle of bleach. I set a box of crackers on the table and found a small travel case to fill with toiletries and clothes. I had just begun searching through my mother's closet in the guest room when the telephone rang.

"Hello?" I said, spying a sweater and pants that she would need.

"Did you see Mom?" It was Ginny. Her voice struck my face like the crunching blow of a prizefighter's fist. My body jolted and I bit my bottom lip, which oozed with blood. It was only the salty taste of my own blood that stopped me from screaming, "HOW COULD YOU LEAVE HER LIKE THAT?!!!"

"Yes," I said flatly, sucking on my lip to stanch the flow of blood. "I'm packing up some clothes right now to bring to her."

"Why?" she asked. "She should have enough clothes in her suitcase."

"I didn't see a suitcase last night," I replied, pressing my tongue and teeth around the lip to stop the throbbing. I opened a drawer and withdrew socks and underwear. "I'll look for it this morning."

Ginny began to recount the events that led to my mother's admission at McLean. I ignored her patter, seething. Nothing she said could justify what I had witnessed the evening before. Nothing. I continued to fill the travel case with clothes and supplies for my mother, glancing at the clock on a nightstand.

"Is there a cafeteria in that building where I could buy her some food?" I asked rudely, interrupting her midsentence. She seemed surprised by my tone but paused to check with Jon.

"No," she said, and drew a breath to finish her story.

"Okay," I said abruptly, "I have to go. I don't have that much time today." I made no attempt at civility. Before I could hang up, she told me that Walter would be visiting our mother that evening.

"Good," I said, "have him bring her a frappe." And I clicked off the telephone.

I drove quickly to the hospital. My long strides covered the distance across the parking lot in seconds. I yanked open the door, stormed up to the ticket window, and told the guard that I knew where to go. The hallway was brightly lit, and the offices assumed the casual atmosphere of a medical office building. I punched in the floor numbers for AB-2 and stood in the elevator, my left foot tapping impatiently on the metal floor. I exited the elevator and reached the nurses' station before the elevator doors had closed. As I marched toward my mother's room, I was greeted by faint screaming from the neighboring room.

Where's your family? my mind snapped.

I stepped around the cardboard box and found my mother sleeping, under covers, on her bed. Her diaper was clean, although I noted a stain on the sheets. Before awakening her to acknowledge my presence, I searched her sparsely furnished room for the suitcase. The closet was empty. There was no sign of the suitcase or her eyeglasses.

I went out in the hallway to search for clean linens. An aide, walking up the hall, stopped me as I jiggled the locked door to a linen closet.

"Can I help you?" she asked.

"I'm Jan Simpson, Muriel Albertson's daughter," I said. "I'm looking for clean linens to change her bed."

"Oh," she replied turning to continue down the hall, "we'll take care of that." I stepped away from the closet and blocked her path up the hall.

"I'm happy to help out," I said unsmiling. "I was here last evening and found her lying on an unmade bed. I'm sure you folks get mighty busy, so I'm happy to help."

She shifted uncomfortably from one foot to the other.

"I have a few questions for you," I said, through gritted teeth.

"Last night, I changed my mother's diaper in her bathroom and noticed that there were no gloves, no soap, and no bleach available. You do know that she has *C. difficile*, an infectious disease, which is why she's in a private room. I know that you don't typically treat medical cases here, so you might not have the supplies you need to keep safe. I brought bleach and gloves from home today, and I'm happy to provide more if you need them. I'll leave them in the bathroom. I certainly wouldn't want any of the staff to get infected." I inhaled slowly and tried to belie my fury by softening my tone of voice. "I'm also looking for my mother's suitcase. Have you seen it? It's blue, and oh, her eyeglasses are missing too. Do you know where they are?" I smiled sweetly.

"No, I don't, but you could check at the nurses' station."

"Okay," I said, stationary and still blocking her path up the hallway. "I also brought some crackers from home. She didn't eat last night, and I want to make sure that she gets something to eat this morning. You know how it is with these old folks," I feigned a laugh, "it's a problem if they take their meds on an empty stomach. Before I feed her, do you know if she has any dietary restrictions?" Her face wore the expression of a trapped animal.

"You'll have to ask her nurse," she said, and her face suddenly appeared relieved, her eyes shifting toward someone coming up the hallway behind me.

I turned, expecting to confront my mother's nurse, but instead came face-to-face with a young man from housekeeping. The aide and he exchanged a long look.

"I'll check with the nurse now," I said, turning back to the aide, my smile frozen and stiff. "Just leave those linens on the chair in my mother's room. I'm going to be here all day, and I like to keep busy." I strode up the hallway, matching my stride with the rhythm of my mother's neighbor's scream.

I waited for the nurse outside the station, scanning a bulletin board replete with medical notices. A middle-aged woman approached, and I extended my hand and introduced myself, adopting a relaxed posture. A good nurse is key to good care; it was imperative that we make a connection.

We chatted conversationally about my mother's treatment, and I briefed her on my mom's medical history and her family situation. I mentioned that my mother had five adult children and eighteen grandchildren, most of whom lived in the area and tended to visit in droves. She smiled appreciatively.

"We'll try to keep the number of visitors down daily, though, and if there's a problem with my family bothering any of the patients, please let Ginny or me know."

"Oh, I don't think that will be a problem," she said kindly. "Few of our patients have regular visitors." *No kidding.*

"I also wanted to ask you about dietary restrictions," I said. "Last night I noticed that my mother's food was, um, not terribly appetizing. May we bring food to her from home?"

"Oh, that's fine, but it won't be necessary. Today she'll be eating lunch with the other patients," she said as we walked toward a large conference room in which chairs were arranged around a rectangular table. "You're welcome to join her."

"Thanks, I will," I said, wanting to check out the menu. "I don't need to leave for home until two o'clock. I'll get her up and dressed in a while, if that's okay." Our conversation ended pleasantly.

Good. My mother's nurse was professional and caring. I began to relax about her care.

I wandered back toward my mother's room and spied a pail and mop resting against the door. Inside the room, the worker from housekeeping was removing the cardboard box. My eyes locked briefly with his and he looked away quickly. I walked discretely to a sitting area at the end of the hallway and stood looking out a window until my mother's room was clean.

By lunchtime, her missing suitcase was found along with her eyeglasses. My mother, dressed in clean clothes with her hair neatly combed, walked with me toward the conference room for lunch.

We were early and only three patients were present. One, an amputee who used a wheelchair, sat up against a wall, complaining and badgering an aide about the food; another, hunched at the end of the table, didn't look up to acknowledge our presence; the third, an older woman with heavy, cumbersome arms, dressed in a housecoat, looked as though she had just stepped away from the stove to serve her family. My mother smiled pleasantly and said hello; the other woman nodded and then looked away, staring at the food on the tray the aide was placing in front of her. They weren't exactly a lively bunch. I was glad I had decided to stay.

We sat at the far end of a table, chatting amicably with an aide who seemed to appreciate our presence. We discovered that she, in fact, lived near Ginny and Jon, a tidbit that made me feel even better about my mother's care. My mother was no longer an unknown, demented old woman with diarrhea, but a frail grandmother, supported by her family and needing their care. She would be all right.

Midway through my mother's meal, an elderly gentleman wandered into the room. He surveyed the table, avoiding the empty seats near the others, pausing at the chair beside my mother.

"May I join you?" he asked, bowing his head slightly.

"Of course," she smiled pleasantly, gesturing elegantly to the empty seat beside her. I grinned and nodded my head. *At last, someone she can talk to.*

He exchanged pleasantries about the food and then began a discourse about his family and a recent move from Texas. As he spoke, I was conscious of the cadence in his voice, professorial in nature, like a man who spent years introducing students to Chaucer, Milton, and Shakespeare. He was charming, eloquent, and gracious. After a bit, I became an unnecessary presence at the table, as he and my mother were engrossed in an animated conversation; she had fits of joyful, carefree laughter I hadn't heard in years. *Oh my God, she's flirting with him!* I looked away so they wouldn't see me smiling.

My mother and he might have been anywhere, seated around my dining room table, in the corner of a restaurant, in line at the grocery store. I was struck by the sheer normalcy of their interaction, even as I knew it was all an illusion. *So, this is what dementia looks like.* On the outside, they seemed perfectly normal, but inside, the synapses in their brains were faltering. *Had he really moved recently from Texas? Or did that happen forty years ago?* It struck me as a bit sad that people as eloquent as this man and as gentle as my mother could age with their memories dissolving, but I was delighted that they had both found some pleasure, however temporary, in each other's company.

When I got home, I called Ron and filled him in on the details of my visit.

"This is going to be the death of me," I said. "One day, I feel like they're going to kill her with their incompetence, and the next day I think she's going to come home with a boyfriend!"

"Have you considered that she might remarry?" Ron teased. "She is, after all, a good-looking woman." I dissolved into laughter.

"Oh, don't joke about that Ron. That's all I would need now!"

*   *   *

After her release, my mother stayed at our house until the day before we left for our summer vacation in New Hampshire. One positive outcome of her McLean visit was that her outpatient care would now be monitored by Dr. Lowell, a female psychiatrist. Despite my first impression of the hospital, McLean is, in fact, one of the finest psychiatric hospitals in America, its faculty affiliated with Harvard Medical School, its research on the cutting edge of advances in mental health care. My family had learned the limits of allowing an internist to supervise my mother's mental health care; we would be better off with a skilled psychiatrist experienced with elderly dementia, and Dr. Lowell was, by reputation, among the best. It would be good to have her help in managing my mother's condition.

During that first week of our vacation, the children and I settled quickly into the languid rhythm of unscheduled summer days. Among my summer reading was a copy of *No Ordinary Time,* an account of President Roosevelt's leadership during the Second World War—beautifully written by historian Doris Kearns Goodwin. One morning before the children awoke, I settled into a chair on the porch overlooking the golf course and watched the sprinklers gloss the green summer grass on the sixth hole and paint the asphalt encircling the course. I flipped open the book cover, startled by a handwritten note from the author to my father that read, "To Bob, I trust you'll enjoy revisiting an extraordinary time in your life." I began to read slowly; the story was so familiar, not only from my history books, but from stories told around my kitchen table. After a few pages, I stared out and across the golf course at the mountains, where the clouds cast shadows on the sloping evergreens. The soft hissing of the water, the patter of drops on the road, and the cool chill of morning air lulled me to another place where I could hear my father's voice talking about the war. Unlike the flood of stories about his childhood, these stories trickled out only occasionally over the years, when we asked him directly or when events in the evening news prompted some stirrings of memory. Katie's voice interrupted my thoughts, "Mommy, can you read to me?" and she handed me a stack of her favorite books. I put the book aside and pulled her onto my lap.

From then on, I woke early, brought my morning coffee to the porch, read a few pages, and reminisced about the parallel stories from my father's life. Pearl Harbor was a turning point for Roosevelt and for the nation, as well as the day my father brought Bill home from the hospital as a newborn. General Patton led the fight in Europe with my Uncle Jack among his troops; Uncle Jack would later spend his first year home in a psychiatric hospital recovering from post-traumatic stress. While the book recounted the inside story of the war and its leadership, I knew the inside story from the perspective of its troops. My dad told stories about the young bucks on the battleships who loved to shoot the 16-inch Mark guns, and the antics of the crews who manned the antiaircraft guns, their adrenaline-driven rush targeting incoming Japanese planes. And while names like General Eisenhower and Admiral Halsey made the news, I knew, as did they, that it was the unspoken bravery of every soldier who won the war, men like my Uncle Art, whose stomach trouble was caused not by indigestion or stress, but by shrapnel released when his ship was bombed.

Days flowed into weeks, and weeks into a month, as I read more slowly, never wanting to reach the book's end. One day, with only a few pages remaining, I stared out at a lone bird circling the golf course and watched it dive sharply down to the red flag fluttering on the sixth hole. When we arrived in New Hampshire, I was still sleeping little, spending long hours in the early morning recalling my father's stories so as not to lose any of them, so not to lose him, for I feared that when I could no longer remember the stories, his personal story would be gone, too. But now I slept soundly through the night. I flipped to the back cover, studied the black and white photos of President and Eleanor Roosevelt, and absentmindedly tapped the cover. I was done grieving for my father, for I knew that whenever I felt that I had lost him, that I had lost the memories of his life, I would again find him, alive and well, between the pages of this book.

The children and I swam and golfed and played tennis at our leisure, studying the constellations at night, relishing county fairs and summer theater. By August, when Ginny joined us for two weeks on vacation, I felt completely restored.

My mother's summer was not as pleasant. As construction continued on her new apartment, the treatment plan to rid her of *C. difficile* failed. With only one bathroom in Ginny's house, other family members were infected as well. I contacted Dr. Fadia and discussed the risk of keeping her on a low dose of vancomycin. He cautioned that, in time, she might develop a vanco-resistant infection, one that could not be cured. The choice was mine. She could continue to battle the infection, remaining housebound and isolated from others, or she could take medicine that would stop the diarrhea, at least for a while, allowing her to maintain an active lifestyle. I made the choice for quality of life, even if it meant a reduction in longevity. My mother and my father had lived every moment of their lives like it was their last. They didn't check out, curl up, or withdraw from life regardless of their medical ailments. My mother was now nearly eighty years old. She was physically able and still socially aware, and it would be a shame for her life to end in isolation. I would take the risk on her behalf. Dr. Fadia prescribed 125 milligrams of vancomycin daily.

Her adjustment to living at Ginny's house full-time had not gone well either. The tension reached a crescendo when my mother decided to return home to her old neighborhood, walking alone out the door and up the street toward the highway that led to her old house. Fortunately, one of my oldest nieces returning home from work spied her grandmother marching along the sidewalk that led to the main road. She cajoled my mother into the car and brought her home unharmed. Everyone became concerned for her well-being since they could not supervise her continually.

At the suggestion of a social worker, Ginny contacted an organization called Cooperative Elder Services that ran elderly day care centers. The centers provided supervision of frail elders and disabled adults by nurses and a skilled staff between 8:30 a.m. and 2:30 p.m. daily. The fees included transportation, activities, lunch, and supervision of medication. Ginny enrolled my mother for three days a week and then called to tell me to anticipate the bill. My initial reaction was not favorable, but I held my tongue. It was not a solution I would have sought had my mother been living with me, but I let it go—Ginny needed the freedom to set up supports that would work for her family. Only later would I come to appreciate Ginny's decision to use this resource, for the day care support from Cooperative Elder Services helped us keep our mother at home until her death.

The summer ended on an upbeat when my mother received three offers for her house. I accepted one and returned from vacation rested and ready for what I was confident would be a fresh start for our family that fall.

EIGHTEEN / Care for the Caregiver

WITHIN THREE WEEKS BACK, I felt like I had never been away. Ginny resumed her daily calls with tasks she needed me to complete, the children had returned to their hectic back-to-school schedules, and I spent every available minute packing the contents of my mother's house to move into her newly finished apartment. One Saturday, I sent Ron over to install a door alarm, one that would activate if she wandered around at night. Her apartment was attached to the side of Ginny's house, and we were not taking the chance of her leaving the house unnoticed again.

"Jan," Ron said, coming into the kitchen having completed the installation, "your mother was still sleeping when I left today." His voice sounded concerned. "It's after one o'clock. That's not like her."

"I think Ginny gives her medication to sleep in on Saturdays," I replied, drying the dishes.

"What? And you're letting her do that?"

"Ron," I sighed, not wanting to get into this now. "Ginny tutors kids all day on Saturday. It's an important part of their income. My mother kept wandering in and out of her sessions, interrupting her repeatedly. She tried to get Carol or Walter to take Mom out on Saturdays so she could work in peace, but they either didn't show up when they were supposed to or they arrived so late it didn't help. What's she supposed to do? She needs this money."

"Well," Ron insisted, "you're going to have to stop that. Your mother cannot spend the day in bed. That's not right."

"I'm not going to give up my Saturday, Ron," I replied wearily. "It's the only day of the week I have to spend with you and the kids as a family. I take her here on Sundays, and I'm spending every day of the week working on her move. That's my priority right now."

"Jan," he persisted, like a bulldog unwilling to let go of his bone, "it's irresponsible to treat your mother like that. What's the matter with you? She cannot be left in bed."

Ron didn't get it. He didn't know what my weekdays were like, how much time I spent addressing my mother's needs. He had enough to do with the pressures of travel and his own work. But that word *irresponsible* rubbed my soul with sandpaper.

"I am not irresponsible, Ron. I know what Ginny is doing, and I won't let it continue for long. But I *need* to handle my mother's move first." *Please give it up. Don't push me right now.*

"I'm sorry," he said. "But you cannot ignore this, Jan. You need to stop it now. It's irresponsible." *There's that word again.* He lit a fuse and the dynamite exploded.

"Irresponsible?" I repeated, my voice growing louder. "How dare you stand there and call *me* irresponsible!" I slapped my hand on the counter so hard that my arm stung with pain. "I spend nearly *every* minute of *every* day caring for her or for her needs! You don't think I know what's going on there? You think that I'm not upset about it? I am! But I *cannot* deal with that right now. I have her house to pack up, the move to plan, meetings with her lawyer and the realtor coming up. I have to get her to the doctor for her checkup and a flu shot. AND there's the small matter of caring for our own kids and this house. *I CANNOT DO IT ALL!*" I was furious and physically shaking; I grabbed the side of the counter to steady myself.

Ron stood impassively on the opposite side of the island in our kitchen. He said nothing for a few minutes after I stopped yelling, breathless, awaiting his response. He stared at me and I stared at him; the silence between us grew whiskers. He returned my gaze silently, his face poker straight. After years of dealing with the sharks on Wall Street, my outburst was tame. He stood silently. I shook with rage.

"I'm going out to wash the car," he said at last.

"*GOOD!*" I yelled, still unable to control my voice. He walked slowly toward the back door.

He turned back toward me as he stepped outside.

"Jan," he said quietly but firmly, "you are going to have to stop this now." He shut the door quickly, as I screeched and threw the dishcloth into the sink. I stomped upstairs toward the laundry room. I slammed open the washing machine and dryer doors, heaving heavy wet towels into the dryer, cursing with each thump.

"Mommy?" Katie's shadow appeared in the doorway. "Mommy, are you okay?" I turned to her and her big brown eyes looked up at me, brimming with tears.

"I'm fine!" I replied angrily.

"Mommy?" that tiny voice again. "Are you and Daddy getting a divorce?" *Oh my God.*

I knelt down beside Katie, drawing her into my arms and rocking her slowly as she cried, nestling her head under my chin so she couldn't see my tears.

"No, honey," I cooed, "Daddy and I are not getting divorced. We hardly spend enough time with each other already."

"But you are really angry with Daddy," she continued, placing her head on my shoulder. "You yelled really, really loud."

"No," I said slowly. "I'm not angry at Daddy, I'm just angry at something he said. I love Daddy, honey." I stroked her cheek. "He just said something about Nana that upset me, that's all."

We continued to rock back and forth in the laundry room until her body no longer quivered. The warmth of her touch soothed my nerves. I forced a smile and encouraged her to join Ron to wash the car.

"He really needs your help," I smiled, gently rubbing her arms. "And I'll be down in a minute, too. As long as you promise not to get me wet!" I tickled her until she giggled with glee. She gave me another hug and kiss and then ran downstairs to help her dad.

I sat on the laundry room floor, knees bent, my head between my arms. *Oh, please God,* I prayed, *this has got to stop before it destroys my family.* I traced the pattern on the floor tiles, over and over, breathing in slowly, praying for strength. *Something has to change.*

Later that evening, Ron brought two glasses of wine into the den.

"So tell me what's going on," he said, refusing to accept my weak response that everything was fine. "You really lost it today; I want to know what's happening."

I proceeded to fill him in on everything. The daily telephone calls, my mother's needs, the growing sense that this commitment I made to my mother meant that the demands on my time and the strain on my nerves was never going to end.

"And now Katie thinks we're getting a divorce."

"She does?" Ron laughed, and then he caught the pained expression on my face. "I'm not going anywhere, Jan, you know that," he said seriously, pulling me closer into his arms.

We brainstormed ways we could put some limits around my time. Ron offered to attend the closing on my mother's house and to plan outings for us as a family for every Saturday evening. I decided that after my mother was settled in her apartment, I would limit my time with her to Thursdays and Sundays, and we would hire help to cover Saturdays.

As the fall unfolded and winter approached, I no longer expected the older siblings to help with Mom. Ginny and I were finding our way. My mother was in elder care three days a week and her new apartment, connected by a hallway off of Ginny's kitchen, reduced some of the pressure on Ginny and her family. Lindsey resumed sleeping in her own bedroom, Ginny used my mother's sitting room as a study for tutoring, and my mother seemed happier puttering around in her own space, surrounded by her belongings. We had begun to create some comfortable routines.

Instead of the daily phone calls, I asked Ginny to start a notebook of errands for me to run on Thursdays; I found a list each week that my mother and I enjoyed completing together. The doctors began to book appointments on Thursdays, and friends offered to drive the kids to their lessons or sports on Thursdays so I didn't have to rush home to meet them after school. On Sundays, I brought my mother to my home, along with my youngest niece so Ginny and Jon could have Sunday afternoons free with their teenage daughters. By limiting face time to Thursdays and Sundays, unless there was an emergency, I slowly regained some control of my schedule.

In November, we held an eightieth birthday party at our home and videotaped my mother with all of her grandchildren so she could watch it later as a reminder. For Thanksgiving that year, Ron, the kids, and I visited New York City and met friends in Manhattan to watch the Macy's Thanksgiving Day Parade. It was a beautiful day, and the kids were delighted to see the floats and the fanfare of marching bands. Our life finally seemed to be approaching some semblance of normalcy.

"Jan," Ron said that Sunday, coming into the sunroom at his parents' house in New York. "You're mother is back in McLean."

I couldn't believe it.

"I swear Ginny waits until we're away to commit her. Let's head home after breakfast. This time, if I find her as I did the last, I am bringing her home."

Since the June admission to McLean, I had let Ginny interact with Dr. Lowell without intervention. Although I had handled my mother's earlier appointments with Dr. Christakos, I thought Ginny should now manage her psychiatric care since she was living with her. This second admission changed my mind.

We drove home quickly and I arrived at the hospital to find her admitted to the same floor, but in a different wing. My mother greeted me somewhat sluggishly, showing me the room that she shared with another elderly woman. Without IV bottles and the equipment typically found in a medical hospital, they looked like college roommates, sharing dorm space with twin beds. I knew without seeing her nurse that she had been given Haldol, an inexpensive and widely prescribed psychotropic drug that had always made her sluggish, without affect. She functioned better with a touch of Risperdal, but it would take an act of God to get the medicine changed without a relationship with her physician. My mother was dressed in a floral blouse and her navy stretch pants; she seemed okay. I went home and visited her early the next morning.

I arrived back at the hospital just as she was finishing a roundtable discussion of current events. Given her medicated state, I'm sure that she said little, but she moved a chair into the hall to join the other patients seated in a loose circle around the edges of the corridor. All but one patient was an elderly woman, and all but one woman wore street clothes. A male psychiatrist moved blithely toward the piano in the corner, pulled out the bench, and began playing an old show tune. It was time for music therapy. He stopped playing for just a moment as song sheets to 1920s and 1930s show tunes were passed around the circle. *Well, isn't this fun!* I knew them all, for as a child my mother had Mitch Miller records that I played repeatedly until I had memorized every song. The psychiatrist played "Ain't She Sweet" and "Give My Regards to Broadway," and I joined the circle and sang with the abandon that makes my children's eyes roll. My mother smiled. It was too bad that I hadn't brought along a pair of large spoons. As a child during the Depression, my mother and her friends would occasionally visit a neighborhood cinema, where the talking film was preceded by a vaudeville show that included some local patrons. My mother, a waif with a sultry voice, was often part of the act, saving her few precious pennies for a candy treat. She played the spoons, and her rendition of Mae West's "Pistol Packin' Momma" was the central act of every family Christmas party for years. My family would have a lot of fun with these old gals on the psychiatric ward, although after the hospital saw all of us in action, they would likely commit my entire family en masse.

In the interludes, I observed the faces of her companions and wondered what these women had done wrong. Gathered around the piano, singing aloud without pitch or care, these elderly women could have been in any number of settings—an assisted living facility, a nursing home, or even at a church supper. How did they end up singing show tunes in a locked psychiatric facility? What crimes have they committed? As the pianist played the prelude to an old family favorite, "Five Foot Two, Eyes of Blue," the answer came with startling clarity. These women had indeed committed a crime, one egregious crime that left them shunned by society and ignored by their families. Their crime? They had grown old.

*   *   *

I needed to meet with Dr. Lowell without upsetting Ginny. After my mother's release, I suggested that Dr. Lowell be added to my Thursday assignments so neither Ginny nor Jon would lose time from work. They readily agreed.

Six years had elapsed since our move back to Boston, during which time I spent many days visiting doctors with my parents. By now, I never went to a doctor's appointment without preparation. I had three objectives for this first meeting with Dr. Lowell. First, I wanted the doctor to see my mother as she typically was, not in the zombielike state we observed when she was in institutional care, but as she was in my home, a pleasant, forgetful, little old lady. Second, I wanted to discuss her medication. And third, I wanted to clarify the roles in our family and how best to communicate medical information to us.

My mother and I sat in the hallway reading magazines awaiting our appointment with Dr. Lowell. Without examining tables or signs pointing to x-ray or the lab, the medical building seemed like any office building, the opened doors revealing doctors' offices that included simply a desk, a few chairs, and filing cabinets. As we waited, the piano-playing psychiatrist walked by, nodding with vague familiarity, prompting a fond smile.

The door to Dr. Lowell's office opened, and a woman about my age stepped out. She introduced herself, shaking our hands, her furrowed brow giving her a permanently worried expression despite her smile. She invited us into her office and took a seat at her desk, my mother beside her. We were joined by a social worker named Marion, who sat to my left, closest to the door. My mother was chatty and sociable, and within minutes Dr. Lowell commented on how well she seemed.

"She runs up and down the stairs like a kid, Dr. Lowell," I offered smiling. "She's in great shape!"

"For the shape I'm in!" my mother retorted, and we four laughed heartily. *Good for you, Mom,* and we had achieved our first objective, even though Dr. Lowell didn't quite get the joke, for my mother was parroting one of my father's favorite one-liners. I handed Dr. Lowell a piece of paper.

"This is a list of my mother's medications and some information you should have in your records," I said, moving on to objective number two. The paper I gave the doctor was a one-page sheet that Ginny had originally started and I maintained. At the top was my mother's name, date of birth, insurance numbers, and next of kin, complete with home, office, and cell phone numbers. Dr. Harmon's contact information followed, along with the vendor and type of pacemaker my mother wore, included at the advice of a cardiac nurse who noted that information was important in an emergency. Next was a list of her medications, including the dosing, sorted by the time of day each pill was taken, along with the drugs to which she was allergic written in bold capital letters. This one-page document was updated any time the information changed and was given to every health care contact we made. We found that this was the easiest way to ensure that everyone had the same information, and it saved us considerable time in searching for numbers or critical information.

Dr. Lowell began to transfer the information into her medical file.

"That's your copy," I said. "I can print another for our records." Dr. Lowell seemed to appreciate the gesture.

I used the paper as an opportunity to briefly review my mother's psychiatric history and to inquire about the transfer of her medical records from Dr. Christakos. I was cautious about talking too much, for an early lesson I learned from my father was how insulting it was to have doctors ignore him and talk to one of his children. My mother was part of this dialogue, and, as a result, I said less than I might have had she not been present.

"Dr. Christakos also found that Risperdal seemed to work better than Haldol for her," I offered gingerly.

I knew that physicians prescribe Haldol often because it is an inexpensive choice, so I reminded Dr. Lowell that my mother had good insurance coverage and that she could prescribe a more effective drug without concern for its cost. There is a fine line between sharing what I hoped was helpful information and dictating instructions to a physician. To her credit, Dr. Lowell did not seem offended by my suggestion, a sign to me of her competence and confidence as a psychiatrist.

"What do you know about Aricept?" I asked, wanting to learn more about this drug from her. We had a quick conversation, as my mother was getting a bit antsy about my chatter. Dr. Lowell indicated that there was little data yet available regarding its efficacy, but that it might become part of my mother's mix of drugs. I made it clear that only she, and no other doctor, would control the mix of psychotropic drugs my mother took, and asked if it was acceptable to have Dr. Harmon call her if he had any questions. She seemed comfortable with that arrangement.

The dispensing of drugs is as much an art as a science. The first order of business is to choose a drug that will address the medical concern, and then determine the dosing appropriate for the patient. Many physicians prescribe lower than the recommended dosing for elderly patients, aware that few clinical studies use elders to qualify a new prescription drug. By carefully monitoring a patient's progress when a new drug is administered, and refining the dosing over time, a person is most likely to achieve the maximum benefit with the fewest side effects. The most capable doctors also understand that the introduction of any new medicine to a patient may require a refinement of the dosing of all of their other prescriptions: like a master chef, they must tweak and refine the blend of all ingredients to create the most flavorful dish. Although patients can read books or talk to pharmacists about drugs and their side effects, there is no replacement for an experienced physician and time to observe the impact of a specific drug regimen on a specific patient.

There was one last objective for this appointment with Dr. Lowell, which was to discuss our family roles. Dr. Lowell sensed my mother's need to talk and began a pleasant conversation with her. Marion, the social worker, quietly asked me about my mother's living arrangement, the roles Ginny and I were sharing, and my mother's use of elderly day care. She encouraged the use of day care and then focused the conversation on Ginny. I was a bit reticent to discuss the strain Ginny surely felt, coping with teenagers, a full-time job, and a forgetful mother. But Marion's interest was professional and compassionate, offering strategies for reducing some of that stress. As I turned back to join my mother's conversation with Dr. Lowell, I admired the holistic way she was managing my mother's care. This was the first time I had met with a physician and a social worker together, and I made a mental note to seek out social workers for advice in the future.

Dr. Lowell and Marion were not only interested in the mental health of my mother, but in the mental health of her caregivers as well. Their approach reminded me of my children's first pediatrician, a man to whom many of the doctors in Princeton sent their children. He scheduled thirty-minute appointments for each well-baby check, during which he spent about ten minutes examining the baby and twenty minutes in his office talking with the mother. After weeks of well-baby visits, I asked him about his approach: in this age of managed care, the twenty-minute visit with each new mother seemed like a waste of his time. His response was compelling, for he observed that the key to a healthy baby was not only his or her well-baby checkups but also a healthy and well-informed mother. He had found that after years of following this practice, his patients had far fewer office visits over the years than children whose physicians rushed mothers and babies through their appointments.

Dr. Lowell obviously followed a similar philosophy: to care for the caregiver as well as the patient. And although my mother would live for four more years, she was never again admitted overnight for psychiatric care at McLean Hospital or anywhere else.

The Author's Guidance

The preceding chapters describe events in the aftermath of my father's passing as we struggled to care for my mother who could not stay alone for more than an hour or two.

Here are some issues for you to consider:

• Sibling Relationships

In an ideal world, siblings have strong, positive relationships with their parents and will work together to support them in the old-old stage of life. More often, however, one or two adult children will bear the most responsibility for the care of aging parents. If that person is you, determine the limits to your role and clarify the support that your siblings are willing to provide over time.

• Spouses and Grandchildren

The caregiving needs of in-laws can place a strain on any marriage. Put a priority on family time, regardless of what may be happening with your parents. Including grandchildren appropriately in the care of their grandparent can strengthen the ties between them. Sometimes, young children can better relate to elderly grandparents as they grow increasingly more dependent.

• The Power of Grief

Until my father died, I had never experienced grief so intense that it left me indecisive and withdrawn. Although time and the needs of my young children eventually cleared the fog, it heightened my awareness of the importance of making critical decisions—about housing, legal authority, etc.—before a death occurs. Scrambling to find documents or to decide who is in charge when a death occurs will only heighten tension among family members. Anger is the first stage of grief. Expect some tension, even if you and your siblings have always been close-knit.

• Medical and Mental Health

Elders die from infection, and repeated visits to hospitals increase the likelihood of them contracting one. If your parent is hospitalized, arrange for friends and family to visit every day, around lunch or dinner, if possible. Build relationships with nurses and social workers who can advise you and them about care. If your parent takes prescription drugs that impact mood or cognition, consult with a geriatric psychiatrist.

• Caregiving: Help for your Parents

How do you feel about providing physical care for your parents? The answer to that question will identify the need to investigate home care, assisted living, or skilled nursing facilities. Start now, and talk with an elder law attorney about asset protection if you have not already done so.

• Caregiving: Help for the Caregiver

Letting go, allowing others to take charge, maintaining connections with friends, laughing, taking vacations—these actions and others are essential if one is to care for a loved one over a long period of time. If you are not the primary caregiver of the ailing parent, then your role is to support the caregiver. Don't ask if you can help, just do it. Bring food, offer to assist with children, help with home maintenance projects, and find ongoing ways to give the caregiver relief.

The Last Years

NINETEEN / A Web of Support

M Y MOTHER HAD ALZHEIMER'S disease. I preferred to tell people that she was forgetful. It wasn't that I was uncomfortable with her illness, but I found widespread ignorance about the disease, ignorance that I encountered with equal measure among health care professionals and the general public. Forgetfulness is socially acceptable; Alzheimer's disease is not.

To many, Alzheimer's means walking brain death, a functioning body with a blank mind. In reality, it's more akin to a flickering light bulb that can be dimmed or enlivened by medications, familiar surroundings, and structured care. It would no doubt surprise some of my mother's family and friends to learn that the elapsed time between the first diagnosis of Alzheimer's and her death was seventeen years. Seventeen years during which she did the laundry, prepared meals, attended parties, laughed at jokes, and loved her grandchildren.

Professionals say that Alzheimer's advances in three stages. During the first stage, the family copes with forgetfulness. Lists need to be made, routines need to be established, driving needs to stop. My mother sailed somewhat easily through this first stage because she had long-standing routines in her life and my father filled in the gaps. In the second stage, forgetfulness leads to confusion, and confusion can lead to outbursts of anger, wandering, and distress. Daily routines, patience, and visual cues help, but the solution that enabled us to keep my mother at home included the carefully monitored use of psychotropic drugs. The pharmacological soup that Dr. Lowell prepared, a base of Paxil, a dollop of Aricept, and a pinch of Risperdal, helped my mother

147

sleep through the night and remain alert though mellow during the day. It took seven months to get the soup ingredients right, seven months during which my mother sometimes slept too much, inverted her days and nights, and became shaky or anxious. Ron was right to be concerned about my mother's sleeping. But our overriding objective was to keep my mother at home. If she slept a bit extra, or needed a pill to help cope with life, so be it.

One morning, a neighbor and I sat over tea in my kitchen chatting about the strain she felt raising three young children. To cheer her up, I told what I thought was a funny story about my mother and her Alzheimer's disease.

"Alzheimer's," she repeated, shuddering. "Wouldn't it be better if she were dead?"

Dead? I wanted to say. Why? Who else would sit for hours matching our orphaned socks? Who would teach my children patience and that forgetfulness is a good excuse for eating dessert before dinner? Who would force me to tap the brakes a bit, to appreciate my physical health? Dead? How might I have experienced the true value of friendship without seeing the monthly letters from her friends who wrote faithfully? When would I confront my own perfectionism, recognize that there are some problems that can never be solved, no matter how much energy or effort or care you put into them? Who would teach me how to take one day at a time, to let things go, that you can laugh and sing songs even behind the locked doors of a psychiatric ward? While my mother might have been unable to function without my family's assistance, she still had much to teach me. Dead? The mother I had known for most of my life, the woman who taught me my prayers and the alphabet, who made my lunch and threw parties and laughed loudly, that woman was dead. She died thirteen years ago. But the shy, nerdy child she once raised was dead too.

"No," I replied simply. "It's not *that* bad." But my friend seemed unconvinced. As I shifted the conversation back toward her children, I wondered if she would have asked if my mother was better off dead if my mother had breast cancer. Again I was reminded of the general lack of understanding about medical diseases that affect the brain. In fairness, though, it had taken me twenty years to both understand and accept my mother's medical status. Surely I couldn't expect my neighbor to reach that same level of understanding over a cup of tea.

My mother knew that she had Alzheimer's disease because I told her.

"Aren't you going to stop by the house?" she asked one day as we drove by her old home on our way back from an errand.

"No, Mom," I said, "You have a new home now. You live in an apartment at Ginny's house. You sold the old house."

"I did?" she said, her forehead creasing into a worried expression. "I don't remember that."

"Well Mom," I said, "sometimes you forget little things. We sold your house so you could build a new apartment at Ginny's. It's a very nice place, and you're now living with your granddaughters." We stopped at a red light and I glanced over at her face.

"Little things?" she said frowning, ignoring my platitudes and staring straight into my eyes. "Jan, I wouldn't call forgetting that I sold my house a 'little thing!'" She had me there. Obviously, all circuits were connected today. I inhaled a deep breath as the light changed to green.

"Mom," I said quietly. "You're right. It's not a little thing, and I apologize for that remark." She nodded forgiveness but continued to look worried.

"We can't really control how we age, Mom," I began, gripping the steering wheel a bit more tightly. "You've always taken care of yourself, and you're in amazing physical shape. For that I'm grateful. Many people your age use wheelchairs, or have bad eyesight, or need a lot of physical care." I could feel her eyes on me.

"But you are aging with forgetfulness," I said. "You're taking some medicine that might help with this, but it is part of how you're going to age." Her eyes widened with realization. The husband of her oldest friend from grammar school had died from Alzheimer's disease, and her girlfriend had died shortly thereafter.

"Now, I don't want you to worry," I continued quickly, my eyelashes fluttering to brush away the tearing. "Ginny and I will keep an eye on you so you don't get into any trouble or get hurt. In fact, that's why you have a nice apartment at her house. We're going to take care of you, Mom, so you don't have to worry about this."

She sat silently and turned her head slowly to look out the passenger window.

"You're the only one who tells me what's going on," she said quietly. I wanted to cry.

"We can't control what's happening to you Mom, but we can control what we do about it. We can sit around upset all day, or we can keep on doing what we have been doing—going out and having as much fun as we can. You are forgetful. We can cry about it, or we can laugh about it. I'd rather laugh about it." She continued to sit silently, turning her face slowly to study mine. I stared at the road ahead.

"Me too," she finally offered with a faint smile. "So, where are we going for lunch?" I laughed, relieved.

As we drove toward the restaurant, I marveled at the way my parents had reacted to serious medical crises. Throat cancer? Fry it. Lung cancer? Cut it out. Alzheimer's? Okay, what's for lunch? By now I fully realized that one secret to longevity is attitude, living your life every day. Deal with the medical issues, certainly, but focus on life. My father used to joke that at his age, every day he woke up was a good one. I saw now that it was not a joke. It was the way he and my mother tackled life, the way they met each crisis. There was no time for self-pity, no time to mope. It was as though the devastation they had witnessed during the Depression and World War II had rewired their souls. For them, it was enough to live, to eat, to breathe, to exist, to laugh. Death was inevitable. So let's have lunch first. And we did. Every Thursday we ate lunch at a different restaurant.

"Ginny wants Dad's car," I told her over chicken salad that afternoon. "It's been sitting in the garage, unused, since we sold your house. Ron just had it in the shop; it runs fine, and it's waxed and ready to be sold. The blue book price is $3,500."

"Don't you think Ginny should have it?" Mom asked.

"No, I do not," I said. I had decided long before this conversation that I would sell any items she no longer used. She needed cash to invest for future home care, not teacups, punch bowls, or a car.

"I should never have given up my license," she sighed, and I tried not to smile at the sight of my mother driving around behind the wheel. "But I think Ginny should have the car." It was her property, after all, and her decision to make. "I want her to pay something for it, though," she continued. "She'll take better care of it if she pays for it." She named a price she thought was fair, too low, in my opinion, and I told her so, but she wouldn't budge.

"And Bill, he wants to buy the cemetery plots in Lynnfield," I added. "You won't need them since you'll be buried in Woburn. They're worth $2,300."

"Oh?" she said, wiping her lips with a napkin. "Tell him to make me an offer."

Make an offer? I had to smile. Perhaps it was the timing of our conversations, the one-on-one discussions over lunch preceded by invigorating outdoor walks that stimulated her mind, or perhaps I was the mother figure around whom she felt secure and comfortable enough to relax and that helped her clarity of thought. Whatever the reason, her judgment, I realized, could still be nuanced and clear. She overrode my decision about the car. She set the price for one child to pay and let another make her an offer. Most importantly, she still wanted to and was able to make these decisions herself.

At the start of the new year, I had begun to use Quicken to track my mother's expenses. The software looks like the register of a checkbook and allows the user to categorize each expense, such as prescriptions or groceries. With a few clicks of the mouse, I could spit out monthly expense reports or summaries of medical expenses needed at tax time. I estimated that my mother's money would run out at age eighty-three or so. Her savings got a boost from the sale of her house, and by carefully watching expenses I hoped to extend her money longer. At tax time, I asked her accountant for a list of qualified medical expenses; he provided me with Publication 502 from the Internal Revenue Service. I knew that we could only deduct medical expenses that exceeded 7.5 percent of her adjusted gross income. So far, her expenses were lower than that number. However, day care and home care would be very expensive and I wondered if any of it would be considered a medical expense.

Publication 502 was a godsend: *You can include in medical expenses amounts paid for qualified long-term care services defined as necessary diagnostic, preventive, therapeutic, curing, treating, mitigating, rehabilitative services and maintenance and personal care services that are: 1) required by a chronically ill individual and, 2) provided pursuant to a plan of care prescribed by a licensed health care practitioner.*

My mother was certainly chronically ill, although she did not yet need more than general supervision of what are called activities of daily living (ADLs) such as dressing, bathing, or toileting. But to my surprise and delight, for this benefit impacts millions of elderly people, the government defined someone as chronically ill who either needed help with ADLs or *requires substantial supervision to be protected from threats to health and safety due to severe cognitive impairment.* All maintenance or personal care services, *care which has as its primary purpose the providing of a chronically ill individual with needed assistance with his or her disabilities,* were a medical expense.

My mother was a safety risk; she could not be left unsupervised. I spoke with Dr. Lowell about the risk factor, and that year, and every subsequent year, she provided me with a letter that described my mother's dementia and included the following statement: "It is medically necessary for her to have twenty-four hour care by family and paid caregivers in order for her to remain in her current setting." With expensive caregiving services looming in her future, my mother could shift resources from paying taxes to paying for home care. It wasn't a significant gain, but every dollar helped. Today, when people ask me at what point I knew that my mother had Alzheimer's disease, I usually joke that I knew when her caregiving became tax deductible.

My mother attended day care on Mondays, Wednesdays, and Fridays. I covered Thursdays, and Ginny hired a sixty-something widow named Helen to help on Tuesdays and a few evenings each week. Weekends remained a problem. We had tried to get our siblings to take Mom out one weekend day a month, but they were inconsistent and undependable. We tried hiring weekend help, but no-shows were problematic. The only sound solution was to use an agency. I scheduled an appointment with an agency in Andover, a half mile from the home in which my father was raised. The small office was nestled between a bridal shop and a funeral parlor. The agency director was pleasant and agreed to an hourly rate of less than half of the fee typically charged by most home care services in our area, because my mother would be using their services indefinitely. We agreed that an aide would arrive at seven o'clock on Friday evenings and stay through seven o'clock on Sunday evenings. I would cover two Sundays a month to save my mother some money.

On the ride home, I thought about my oldest siblings and how I had resigned myself to the fact that Ginny and I would handle our mother's care. But to pay for a buddy to go out with for lunch and exercise seemed ludicrous. *How hard would it be for the others to bring her over to their house one day a month?* My oldest sister worked, but her children were grown, and my brother Walter had essentially retired in his forties having invested wisely in Boston real estate. *He found time to take Mom's piano for his daughter, to pester me for a watch and an old coin, but he can't bring Mom out for one day?* The tension caused a familiar ache in my left shoulder. By the time I arrived home, I was calm again. My mother had the resources, and I would find more. Ginny and I needed this third pair of hands to reduce our stress and have weekends more or less free.

Later that day I went out to my mailbox and found a letter from my brother. The handwriting on the letter was so distinctive that I knew who it was from even before opening it. The return address read "the poor relatives." I did not appreciate the joke, and the note inside added fuel to the fire.

Hi Jan,

Just a quick note to let you know what I spent on the piano fiasco at Mom's prior to closing. I spent approximately $75 for the lumber and nails, etc. to take out the steps and repair them after the movers left and $600 for the piano movers. They said it was more work than they originally thought, and, of course, because they underestimated the job, we would have to pay more $. So, that's it. Please make the check out to Judy, since she spent the majority of the money. Hope you're having a good summer,

Walter

TWENTY / End of Life: What's It Like?

"HOW DO YOU DIE FROM ALZHEIMER'S disease? I want to understand some of the decisions that I might have to make for my mother." I stood next to my sister-in-law Joan at the kitchen sink as we cleaned dishes following a family dinner. Joan is a physician and she could help me answer some important questions. I knew that Alzheimer's was a terminal illness, but I didn't know what it looked like near the end.

Stacking the plates in the dishwasher, Joan explained that the progression of the disease varies by patient, but the end has a similar pathology.

"She'll likely become bedridden," she explained, rinsing a plate and adding it to the rack, "and along with that often comes decubitus ulcers, septicemia, and other infections."

"And my decision there?" She said there weren't any decisions to be made at that point beyond providing palliative care.

"She may contract pneumonia," Joan continued, lining the bottom rack with dirty glassware.

"Do I just let that go?" I asked in disbelief as I opened the refrigerator and found the ground coffee.

"No," she replied, "you'll want to treat the pneumonia with antibiotics, but you might choose to not allow her to be ventilated. If the antibiotics work, then she gets better. If not..." She didn't finish the thought, turning back toward the sink for the dirty utensils.

"Pneumonia is called the old person's blessing," she continued, trying to lighten the dark tone of this conversation. "It's not the worst way to die." *I'll take your word on that*, I thought as I put the filter into the basket of the coffee maker.

"What else?" I pressed, finding a clean spoon in a drawer. "She has a pacemaker. A couple of years ago, the battery died and had to be replaced. In a few years, I might be asked to replace that battery again. Should I say no? Would her heart simply slow down and eventually stop?" I envisioned long naps and a peaceful death.

"I don't know," she said, filling the dishwasher with detergent. "She has A-fib." Atrial fibrillation is an irregular heart beat. "She might have a major stroke, and that's not what you'd want to have happen. You should ask her cardiologist." Joan locked the door of the dishwasher and turned it on.

"Anything else about Alzheimer's?" I asked, counting spoonfuls of ground coffee into the filter as Joan found some plates for dessert. The conversation was making me feel a bit nauseated.

"She may lose her swallowing reflex," she said, and I paused, the spoon suspended in midair.

"Swallowing reflex?" I repeated, placing the spoon carefully on the counter. I had never thought about swallowing before; if I had I would have guessed that we came wired for swallowing, that it was automatic, like a heart beat or an inhaled breath. "It's something we can lose?"

"Yes," she continued, unaware of my discomfort. "She could aspirate food." *Choke, in other words.* "And a decision would need to be made about a feeding tube."

"I see," I said, flipping on the coffee. I had heard enough.

On the ride home, I stared out the passenger window.

"You're awfully quiet," Ron said.

"I'm just thinking," I replied, smiling faintly. "I'm tired; I'm going to take a nap." I shut my eyes so I could think without interruption.

I reflected on my conversation with Joan. I had wanted to know what the endgame of Alzheimer's looked like, but Joan's words reflected the harsh reality of this disease. It was unlikely that my mother would be one of those lucky elders who died in her sleep— hers would be a slower death—death from infection, choking, or drowning on lung fluids. I felt sickened, and the knowledge that I would be involved in making decisions about her death was disturbing.

After my father's death, I lost all illusion that medical professionals make end-of-life decisions. They do not. The advances in medical treatment, coupled with increasing concern about litigation, have shifted the burden of choice from the professional to the family. It would be my call, and in the darkened car I shook my head slowly, gently biting my lower lip. I sighed. I had been through this before on the day my father died.

It was a Thursday, and my daughter had invited a new friend over for a playdate. Her friend's father had come along for lunch, and we had just finished our sandwiches when the telephone rang. The girls were in our basement playroom.

"Hello?" I said.

"Is this Jan Simpson?"

"Yes it is."

"Hi Mrs. Simpson, this is Dr. Wilson calling." My mind snapped to attention, the kitchen fading into a darkened blur. Dr. Wilson was my father's attending physician. "I am sorry to tell you that we removed your father from the ventilator this morning, but he is not responding well. His oxygen levels are dropping. We need to put him back on the ventilator again, but he is insisting that we do not do so. Obviously, under these circumstances, I cannot allow him to make that decision alone."

"I understand," I said and I closed my eyes and inhaled slowly. "He never wanted to be stuck on a respirator." I was buying myself time to think.

"Well," the doctor repeated, "he has asked us not to ventilate him again, but we need the family to agree on that decision."

"I understand," I said numbly, my eyes brimming with tears. I blinked a few times to wash away the tears. "Please, tell me what his words were, exactly."

"Well," the doctor said, adding somewhat apologetically, "and these are his exact words, 'Don't put that damn thing back in my throat!'" I laughed sadly.

"Yep, that sounds like him." I pulled myself together with a sigh. "You need to know that my father does not have dementia. His

mind is sharp and he knows exactly what he's asking you to do."
I drew in a deep breath, shaking my head slowly. "I want you to
honor his request, Dr. Wilson," I said, running my hand through
my hair. "Do not put him back on the respirator."

"Okay," Dr. Wilson replied. "There are some papers you'll need to
sign."

"Do I have time to get there?" I asked. "It might take me a half
hour or so."

"Yes," he said. "It's hard to say how long he'll have, perhaps
twenty-four to thirty-six hours."

"I'll be there as fast as I can," I said, and I hung up the telephone
quickly.

"Oh, Marvin," I said, surprised to see this stranger sitting at my
kitchen table. "Um, my father is dying. Can you make sure that the
girls don't come upstairs for a few minutes? I need to make some
calls." *Welcome to my life.*

I called Jon, who told me that my mother and Ginny were on
their way to the hospital. Carol and Walter had been contacted, but
they couldn't reach Bill. I asked Jon if Katie could stay with him
while I went to the hospital, and he readily agreed. I called a friend
to take Eric home from school and reached Ron in New York City. I
then called my brother Bill.

"I can't leave right away," Bill said, indicating some issues with
one of his kids.

"I don't know how long he'll last Bill," I said, and we repeated a
conversation we'd had the weekend before when Bill came home
to stay with our mother. Whatever happened, I was not to worry
about my brother, he had had time to say his goodbyes.

I arrived at the hospital within the hour, using the drive to shut
down my emotions. I had no idea what to expect. I had never seen
someone die before, and I needed to be mentally strong for my
mother.

The Intensive Care Unit (ICU) was isolated in a wing of the
hospital off a small waiting room. I buzzed for permission to enter,
and was greeted at the door by Ginny.

"I had them start a morphine drip," she said quietly, and I

nodded silently in response. My father's nurse rushed to meet me, seemingly flushed and anxious.

"I want you to know that your father wanted to get off the ventilator," she said breathlessly. "I heard him tell the doctor not to reinsert the tubing."

"I know," I replied. "He never wanted to end this way."

"For the past few days, we've had to keep him sedated," she continued. "Each time the sedative wore off, he tried to pull out the tubing."

"I'm not surprised," I said, appreciating her input. It was reassuring to hear that she confirmed the doctor's comments, but she seemed flustered. Soon, I discovered why.

"You cannot do this to Dad!" Carol barked as I walked toward my father's room. The nurse shooed us out of the ICU and back into the small waiting area. The door locked behind us.

Walter was there too, and both Carol and Walter were upset. They did not agree with the decision to remove the respirator. But it was too late for debate.

"Bill has to be here!" Carol said emphatically.

"He may not be able to," I responded, not wanting to talk to them now. I had to get in that room. I had to sign those papers. I needed to do it soon, before I allowed myself time to think, to vacillate. I had a mission. There was no choice.

"You handle this," I said to Ginny, buzzing the intercom to re-enter the ICU. "You're the psychologist."

Inside, I signed the papers and found my mother standing beside my father's bed. Within a few minutes, the others joined us. I did not look any of them in the eyes.

They did not know. They did not know that it was not my choice. My choice would have been different. My decision would have been to let my father live. It was too soon for him to die. He was helping me raise my children. They were young and still needed their grandfather. They needed his jokes and his laughter. They needed his smooches and high fives. There were more cribbage games to play, more books to read, a crossword puzzle to finish, and French fries to snitch. I wanted to hear his stories again, about his father and his brothers, and his one-liners. I wanted more time, even if that time was colored by disease. I didn't care. It wasn't fair. It was too soon. I did not want to sign the paper.

But he wanted to die, to die then, when he was still able to make the decision—when he was still whole, when our memories would be filled with laughter, not the pain of watching his body bloat and fail. He wanted to die before the cancer spread to his brain. He wanted to spare my mother the pain of watching her husband die slowly and painfully. He knew what the endgame of lung cancer looked like since his mother and a brother had died from the disease. He wanted to call the shots, now, today. He didn't fear the suffering—he lived with constant pain. He simply knew it was his time to die.

I should have known, too. I should have known that the end would come like this. I should have been prepared. But I wasn't. I didn't know that when I agreed to help him that I would be choosing the day of his death. I didn't know that the decision to withdraw life support, shifting from the doctor to me, would alter my response to my father's death from normal grief to trauma. I didn't know that the few angry words spoken by my siblings, a reflection of their own shock and denial, would lead to months of sleepless nights, revisiting my father's last few days over and over, questioning my decision to let him die. It would be more than a year before I could agree with Ron that the doctors had led me toward this decision, knowing that it was the most humane choice for him, avoiding the last few weeks or months of suffering and pain. It was more than a year before I forgave myself for not knowing— not knowing how you die from lung cancer, not knowing that the cancer had in fact spread to his single remaining lung, not asking the doctors the hard questions.

It would not be like that for my mother. I would know. I would be prepared. I would not live in denial or ignorance. And so, I asked Joan the painful questions about the end.

And that information was helpful. Now, I knew that our instinct to keep my mother physically active was important, not only for her memory but also for her physical well-being. Mobility prevented infection. Mobility reduced the likelihood of bladder infections and pressure sores. Mobility pushed back the day when she would become bedridden, for her death would follow soon thereafter.

So my mother walked, every day, until the day she died. She sat in a recliner, she moved from chair, to table, to bed. She never owned a wheelchair and never spent a full day in bed.

"Tell me about feeding tubes," I asked Dr. Harmon during one of my mother's medical visits. "How, exactly, do you give someone a feeding tube?" Dr. Harmon described two choices, one in which the tube is inserted through the nose, the other through an incision in the side. I squirmed at the details, but the details were important. I asked him his thoughts on a feeding tube for my mother.

He thought the feeding tube would be the wrong decision, describing the complications and the caregiving challenges. So, the decision was made, not under pressure in the midst of a medical crisis, but in quiet consultation in her doctor's office. I knew what the choice would be, if and when I needed to make that choice. And I could live with the outcome of my decision, for it was made thoughtfully, with full knowledge of the alternatives, and upon the recommendation of her physician.

I needed to go back to work, but it was impossible for me to return to consulting. I had lunch with a friend, Carrie, who was launching a wellness clinic, and I offered to help her one day a week. To learn more about holistic health practices, we spent a weekend at the Omega Institute, taking yoga and meditation classes. In those sessions, I was reminded how much my physical health was deteriorating—I couldn't even stretch much beyond my knees. In recent years I had battled upper back and shoulder pain. I often slept with a heating pad, sought out a rheumatologist, tried physical therapy, and assumed I was just aging with aches and pains.

"I think the stress that you have internalized over the past few years has settled in your back," Carrie offered, when I observed how great I felt after a yoga class. She recommended more yoga and I joined a class when I got home. The silent, soothing stretches at the end of the hour often put me to sleep on the floor.

If the strain of helping my parents had caused physical aches and pains, the psychological impact, incremental and subtle, was even more damaging. When we moved back to Boston, I was thirty-eight years old and my children were three and three months, respectively. I easily carried the burden of childcare, like an animal in the wild, whose offspring clamber all over her, my son on my back, my daughter in front, my hands free to continue working. At that time, my parents needed the occasional helping hand, a ride to the doctor's office, homemade soups and casseroles for their freezer. Three years later, my burdens shifted, my father climbing onto my back, my mother grabbing frantically to him, my daughter on my shoulders, my son holding my hand. I could no longer work, but I assumed that eventually those burdens would lighten. After five years of elder care, my children now ran ably by my side, needing only the occasional helping hand. But Ginny and I carried my mother's full weight, and my back and shoulders, once straight and strong, were weary.

The spark of determination, the enthusiasm that once propelled me beyond my expected station in life, was diminishing, replaced by the knowledge that the choices I had made to assume caregiving responsibilities forged an unanticipated path. I would care for my children, then my parents, then my teenagers, then my husband, and then I would need caretaking and die. The time between stages of my life had collapsed.

My days were routine, filled with laundry, bills, homework, volunteer work, and medical appointments. I neither rushed through any activity nor anticipated any change, knowing that the next day and the next would bring more of the same. I was no longer on a sabbatical from my career, but retired, and the mirror and the bathroom scale reflected the shift. I wore unfashionable wire-framed eyeglasses, not unlike those of my mother, and dressed in colorless blouses and slacks. I nodded without surprise at the waitress who observed the family resemblance between my mother and me, and I ignored the car dealer who thought I was Ron's mother. Instead of offering a joke or a sarcastic remark, I was apathetic. My life was no longer mine—it now revolved around the needs of others. Instead of anger or frustration, I felt only deep resignation.

"You look like one of those old ladies in the waiting room at the hospital," Ron's brother, a physician, teased at Thanksgiving, as I pulled out some knitting.

"Well," I smiled wanly, "I'm closer than you think."

TWENTY-ONE / Growing Frail

WE MADE A FEW CHANGES in my mother's caregiving, prompted by changes in her deteriorating physical condition. Helen, the widow who helped us on Tuesdays, offered to stay overnight on weekdays to supervise my mother round-the-clock. We kept my mother in day care twelve hours a week, giving Helen time off to compensate for the occasional nights of interrupted sleep when my mother awoke agitated and distressed. I continued to cover Thursdays and two Sundays each month, using aides from the agency to fill in the balance of time. My mother's home care fees now exceeded her pension income, and I began dipping into the savings from the sale of her house.

I had grown to appreciate the nurses at the elderly day care center. Lori, my mother's nurse, wrote notes or called with weekly updates, and, more often as my mother's cognitive behavior or physical condition shifted. It was comforting to us that my mother's vital signs and medical status were reviewed each week by a competent nurse. While we might inadvertently miss something, her nurse would not. Lori's support certainly reduced my stress, and over the next two years, she would become my strongest advisor.

My mother's physical changes were subtle at first. On Thursdays, she began to grow tired by lunchtime. I started to bring lunch and limit errands to the morning. We developed a new afternoon routine, warming our bodies with tea and homemade soup, and then taking afternoon naps, she in her recliner and me in its companion, both snoring softly in the afternoon sun.

"Speed limit thirty-five," my mother said one day on our way to the store.

"I'm only going thirty," I replied, assuming she was subtly telling me to slow down.

"No turn on red," she reported a few minutes later at an intersection. I looked over at her, and then I understood. My mother was becoming less conversational, initiating fewer discussions. Reading street signs was her way of engaging me in a dialogue and letting me know that she could still read. Her behavior was familiar—in kindergarten, both Eric and Katie read signs aloud too. I responded with gusto to her comment.

"Yes, Mom," I said, delving into the particular state laws and proper road behavior. "There's a new law in Massachusetts about turning on red traffic lights." She nodded and spoke in short phrases throughout my dissertation.

Over time, I developed monologues worthy of the best tour guides in Boston. "On your right, Mom, is the Old North Bridge and the Minuteman statue," I noted, delivering a lengthy discourse on the American Revolution, its battles, and its leaders.

"Yield," she replied.

"Yes," I nodded. "That sign says yield. We have a lot of these yield signs in Concord, left over from the days of horse-drawn wagons."

Soon, she could no longer sign her name. I anticipated that change, as each Thursday I had found something for her to sign, birthday cards, checks, gift tags. Initially, she remembered her full name, then she signed with prompting, and then finally not at all. Fortunately, the power of attorney (POA) she had signed years before allowed me to access her bank accounts as needed to pay her bills and manage her money. I signed her tax return on her behalf and included a copy of the POA.

She still visited our house two Sundays each month. Instead of helping me with dinner as she had in the past, she now napped, went for walks, and enjoyed Katie's plays performed with her friends in our family room. I slipped my mother a few quarters to pay the performers and with little encouragement, had the girls deliver encore performances that my mother enjoyed with fresh eyes. We played Fish and Scrabble Junior, which included words on the game board, and I found sixty-piece jigsaw puzzles and watched as my mother assembled kittens and puppies or creatures of the deep.

Sunday dinners had become lengthy affairs. She ate slowly, chewing each bite for several minutes. I began to excuse the children after half an hour and purchased some yarn to knit while she finished eating—it seemed a more polite option than whipping out a laptop computer and paying bills.

"I didn't know you could knit," Ron had said, amused, the first time he saw the knitting needles.

"I haven't knit in twenty-five years," I replied, noting that we could use an afghan for our den. Within a few months, we had an afghan in the den and one in every bedroom. I found a knitters' group online that made booties and caps for premature infants. I could finish a bootie during one of her naps and a cap over Sunday dinner.

*   *   *

It was spring break, and Ron had arranged for our family to visit Walt Disney World in Florida. We wandered around the Universal Studios theme park too, riding through the *Men In Black* exhibit repeatedly, being spooked by the great white shark from *Jaws*, and playing the arcade games.

"Ooh, Mommy look, there's Pikachu!" Katie cried pointing to a yellow stuffed animal behind one of the booths. "Please, Mom, can you win it for me?" I looked at the sign on the booth: LET ME GUESS YOUR AGE. Ugh. I had seen this booth out of the corner of my eye while waiting for the children to finish another game. The college student minding the booth was good. I had watched him turn away several people, accurately guessing their age within three years. I tried to dissuade Katie. I felt sixty-five, I was sure that I looked at least fifty, and I didn't need to hear it from a stranger. But Katie was insistent.

I gave the kid my money and stood wide-eyed as he scrutinized my face, staring at the corners of my eyes. *Cripes, how did I let her convince me to do this?* I stood stiffly, trying not to move, as if proper posture would hide the gray hairs and laugh lines.

"Thirty-eight," he said, and I laughed aloud.

"Oh, honey!" I giggled, handing him my license, "You're off by several years, but I should give you a prize!" He took down the stuffed Pikachu and handed it to me. While Katie has, by now, outgrown the doll, it's one relic of her childhood I can't quite bring myself to give away. It was time to stop the self-pity.

I registered for two alumni seminars at Harvard Business School. The first was aimed at encouraging graduates toward work in nonprofits, in what they called social enterprises. I sat next to an alumna who told me that a few years earlier she had adopted a disabled child, a comment that in the past might have elicited a polite nod and a smile, but now elicited profound respect and admiration. I understood the time involved in supporting someone who is chronically ill. I knew that her commitment meant sleepless nights, disrupted days, and unpredictable schedules. Unlike mine, however, her commitment would not end in her lifetime. My involvement with my parents had an end point, a time in the future when I would recapture my freedom, but this woman would never regain her personal freedom. She would spend the rest of her lifetime caring for another person. That she willingly sought out and accepted that responsibility left me speechless.

We skipped the luncheon speaker to eat our sandwiches on a bench near Harvard Square, taking advantage of the warm spring day.

"So," I said after a while, "how do you keep sane?"

"I write fiction," she said, and we discussed the upcoming publication of her first book. It turns out that she had never aspired to be a published author; she had begun writing simply as an outlet for her energy and creativity. Over time, however, she had found her voice and also work she could fit in around the demands of caregiving. She encouraged me to do the same, to write about my parents, to share the lessons I had learned about elder care.

A few months later I sat in the same classroom, attending a seminar designed for alumnae entitled *Charting Your Course: Working Options,* a program aimed at helping alumnae reflect on career choices as they balance work and family responsibilities. As

I anticipated, the seminar was filled with young alumnae, one of whom anxiously discussed her future, juggling a high profile career with young children. It was hard to empathize. *I've seen your future,* I thought wryly, remembering the singing elders at McLean, *and it ain't pretty.* Later, in a small group discussion, I shared my plans to write a book and to develop an educational series for women, led by women, about the financial, legal, and caregiving issues surrounding retirement and aging. They were largely skeptical, suggesting I hire a writer, and were doubtful I could compete with large established firms who already offer financial and estate planning services. Instead of being discouraged, I took their skepticism as a challenge. The spark inside rekindled.

*   *   *

It was fall and my mother's health was deteriorating. One day, Lori mentioned that I might start looking into a DNR order. A DNR order, Lori explained, was a document that told health care practitioners what to do if a person went into respiratory failure. DNR stood for "Do Not Resuscitate," meaning that if my mother began to struggle with breathing, the attending doctors, nurses, or ambulance drivers were not to ventilate her. In effect, they were not to stand between her and death. Lori said that if we made that decision, she would need a copy of the paperwork at the center.

Not long after, I met with Dr. Harmon to complete the paperwork. I found plastic sleeves at a stationery store, made three copies of the DNR, and prepared three information packages. I inserted the DNR order in the plastic protector along with a medical bracelet that would be attached to my mother's wrist in event of an emergency. Behind the order I placed the one-page document listing next of kin and medications, a copy of the power of attorney, and her health care proxy.

I brought one packet of information to the day care center, I put the second one in a notebook on a table in my mother's apartment, and I kept the third in my office desk. In an emergency, I didn't want anyone to rush around looking for paperwork—they could simply grab the plastic sleeve that held all the information needed to make appropriate medical decisions.

The next Thursday, I asked my mother, resting in her recliner, if she wanted to go out shopping. On most Thursdays, her eyes would light up and she would pop out of her recliner with a little assistance, eager to go run errands. Today she replied that she would rather sleep, appearing less aware of who I was. I sat and knit for a while, watching her twitch. Her left hand appeared atrophied, like she was holding a ball of tissues, as she stretched out repeatedly and grasped the air or reached down toward the floor. She spoke aloud in short phrases, unintelligible syllables, and word fragments. She was not sleeping, just withdrawing into her own world.

After twenty minutes or so, I decided to take her out for an errand anyway, hoping that the walking would allow her to rest more soundly. I roused her and helped her stand. She was weak, needing leverage from me to stand and stay standing. As Lori had reported, there had been a significant change in her physically and she was indeed at risk for falling. We went into the bathroom and I left her seated on the toilet. When I returned, she was at the sink washing her hands, but her underwear and pants lay on the bathroom floor. I helped her dress, found her jacket, and opened the door to the stairs leading to the garage. In the past, as a safety precaution, she walked downstairs while I stood in front by about four or five steps. Today, I walked one step ahead, coaching her all the way down. If she tripped, she would immediately fall onto my back. I opened the car door, and she got in slowly.

During the ride to the grocery store, I tried to make conversation but she ignored my chatter, seemingly more interested in the bottom button of her jacket. I parked near an abandoned shopping cart, walked around the car, and opened her door. In the past, she would swing her legs out, and my support was more of a kindness than a necessity. Today was different. She could not get her left leg out without my help. As we stood with the door opened, a gust of wind blew up, swirling dust around us, and I pulled the hood of her fall jacket up and tied it tightly around her head to break the wind. It was minutes before we moved the few feet to retrieve a carriage.

I asked her to guide the cart with me, reminding her to open her left hand. She continued to focus on adjusting her hood, mumbling fragments of speech. Finally, we made slow progress across the parking lot. As we neared the entrance, she stopped, staring at the doors. It was unclear to her which side to enter and she did not respond to prompts. After several minutes of encouragement, we moved through the entrance. I removed the hood from her head and unzipped her jacket a bit.

We shuffled along the main aisle, past rows of cupcakes and cookies, which she watched with fascination, stopping to examine each package. I allowed her to take one package so we could move on, which she did after considerable prompting, and we shuffled along the front of the store, looking for the cereal aisle. It would be another twenty minutes before we reached aisle thirteen.

After our shopping, we put our few purchases into the trunk of the car and went home. Once again, she wanted to sleep, but her sleep was still fitful. I covered her with a white afghan and sat in a neighboring recliner to knit and observe her behavior. She began to rub sections of the afghan together repeatedly, as if cleaning it with soap. I thought she might have been mimicking my knitting. Later, she took the edge of the afghan and began to rub the side of her recliner, as if she was polishing the arm or cleaning stains with a rag. I told her that I would prepare lunch for us, but I received no response. While the soup cooked, she closed her eyes and fell into a sound sleep.

I woke her for lunch and brought her into the bathroom before we ate. I left her alone while I arranged the soup bowls on the kitchen table, and when I returned, she was absentmindedly wiping her legs with toilet paper. I helped her out of the bathroom and back to the table where she sat and ate her soup very slowly, raising her spoon unsteadily to her mouth. My oldest niece, who was home early from her college classes, came into the kitchen for a banana.

"Do you want a piece, Nana?" she asked sweetly. My mother nodded, and her granddaughter broke off an end of the banana and fed her a piece, like mother to child.

That afternoon, I walked laps with my mother around the house. As we walked, she focused on minutia: the dust on plants, white lint on the floor, leaves on the back deck, pictures on the refrigerator.

We had clearly moved on to the next level of Alzheimer's disease. Before this, my mother's world had included shopping and an interest in car rides. Today she focused only on one detail of life at a time, her peripheral vision obscured, her world now seen through a peephole. What was the difference? What had changed? Was it just one more blockage in her brain? Another tangle?

During the ride home I felt a familiar pain in my left side. I stretched my back, reflecting on the image of my niece feeding her grandmother. My eyes filled with tears, tears of gratitude for my sister Ginny, for her willingness to allow my mother to live with her, in a place surrounded by love and comforted by familiar faces. The physical changes in my mother were very painful for me to watch—I did not have the ability to withstand the strain of watching her health decline slowly every day. Ginny and Jon understood that, and so they took my mother in, giving me the distance I needed to do what I do best—intercede with the doctors, manage the money, support her care. By each doing our part, we would together continue to care for our mother.

TWENTY-TWO / So Long, Self-Pity

I
T WAS CHRISTMAS. My mother was now grandmother to eighteen and great-grandmother to ten. It was my year to host our annual Christmas party, and while Ginny offered to bring the aide to help with Mom, I told her no. Ron and I moved a recliner into our sunroom near the Christmas tree so if my mother needed a nap or a quiet place to relax, we could shut the doors and she could enjoy the twinkling lights or close her eyes and sleep.

The party energized my mother. She sat and watched the loud antics of her grandchildren, hooting over the gifts in the grab; she ate a full meal including dessert; and she posed happily for photographs with her children and grandchildren. While Ron tended the food, I tended to her needs, discretely taking her to the bathroom when the others were occupied. She was upbeat and engaged.

I learned a lot about living with chronic illness by watching Ron's parents age. The most important lesson was not a medical one, but an attitudinal one. Ron's father had lived with multiple sclerosis (MS) for more than forty years. I had been part of his family for sixteen of those years, during which time his medical crises became increasingly more serious. Never once, however, did I hear any of his family refer to him as handicapped. He used a wheelchair. He struggled with a wide array of complications from MS. But he never lived like a disabled man, but rather an able man living with a devastating disease. Each time we were together we talked about the stock market and business, we joked about politicians and liberal women, and we enjoyed many cups of coffee chatting about his family. His illness was the elephant in the room, squeezed into the far corner, and acknowledged only when it thrashed about.

We treated my mother in a similar way, assuming that she was able to read, to walk, to feed herself, to make decisions, until she proved herself unable to do so. And at that point, we adjusted her care, took stock of her strengths, and moved on, assuming that she would tell us, either by words or actions, when she lost more ability. So far, like Ron's father, she was defying the odds. Surely there were more moments when she appeared disconnected from us, withdrawing into her own world, sometimes in a seizurelike state, unable to be roused or distracted. But on some days, days like that Christmas, she was focused, observant, and engaged. I took each moment as it was, appreciating the times of higher lucidity.

I tucked an afghan around her after everyone had left our house and encouraged her to nap in the recliner. Ron and I chatted happily in the kitchen, cleaning up the dishes, when suddenly there was a loud crash. Ron's eyes met mine in a startled gaze.

"Oh my God!" I gasped, heading for the sunroom. "I never should have left her alone!" I swung open the door with Ron on my heels.

The Christmas tree lay on the floor, its branches snapped, glass ornaments shattered around the room. And there, just inches away from the broken branches, was my mother, snoring gently in the recliner. Ron and I shrieked with laughter. Hearing our voices, my mother awoke, unappreciative of the interruption of her nap. We moved her chair to the den where she could resume sleeping.

"Next year, remind me to secure the tree to the wall!" Ron said between chuckles, and we spent the rest of the night cleaning up the mess.

*   *   *

Three weeks into the new year, my mother tripped and fell. It was early Sunday morning, about two thirty. According to the weekend help, she had been restless and got out of bed unattended, falling on her way to the bathroom. The aide, however, neglected to tell Ginny and Jon about the fall, and it was noted only when Helen observed bruising on her face and shoulders Sunday evening. The aide's negligence was reported to the agency and she was replaced immediately.

My mother took Coumadin, a blood thinner, to help prevent

strokes. That medicine made her particularly vulnerable to internal bleeding from falls, and, on Monday, Helen became increasingly concerned, noting that my mother's right eye was drooping and the bruises on her shoulder and body were intensifying. She brought my mother to the emergency room at the Lahey Clinic, where she was admitted with a diagnosis of pneumonia. That afternoon, Walter called to see how Mom was doing and volunteered to stop by and see her for me—Katie had a fever of 102°, so I couldn't leave her alone. He called later that evening.

"I just left the hospital," he said, sounding exasperated. I glanced at the kitchen clock: it was after nine o'clock. "When I arrived at five thirty," he said, "she was still in the emergency room."

"From early this morning?"

"Yeah, apparently no one signed the consent form." I felt a quick wave of guilt thinking of my poor mother waiting for hours in the emergency room because no one had authorized her admission.

"Oh, Walter," I said apologetically, "I didn't know that. No one called me, or I would have run over."

"Well, I signed the forms," he said. "And I waited with her until she got into her room. I had to cancel my plans for tonight." I sighed.

After our father died, Walter had made it clear that he thought our mother belonged in a nursing home, but over time he had become appreciative of our arrangement for her and did what he could to be helpful. Before her apartment was finished, he drove our mother between houses to save Ginny and me the trip during the week. When she was hospitalized, he always visited, bringing an ice cream frappe along with jovial stories for her and the nurses. And although he didn't spend anywhere close to the number of hours Ginny and I did with our mother, he was, in fact, still caring and considerate of her needs.

The next day, I brought Katie with me for a quick visit to check on my mother. Her attending physician recommended that we take her off Coumadin because the risk of hemorrhage from falling outweighed the risk of a stroke. I made a note to check with Dr. Harmon. A social worker also stopped by to meet me, recommending that we consider moving my mother to a rehabilitation center with a memory unit. To her surprise, I said that I would prefer to bring her home, knowing how poorly she fared in institutions. The social worker understood but explained that keeping my mother at the Lahey Clinic for three nights allowed us to move her to a facility within thirty days of her release and still be eligible for Medicare coverage for up to one hundred days. I had no intention of moving her to an institutional setting without inspecting it first, but I appreciated having that option.

This social worker connected me with the Visiting Nurse Association (VNA) of Middlesex-East, who sent out a nurse, social worker, physical therapist, and an occupational therapist. The therapists gave us a list of daily exercises to build strength and hand flexibility, such as rolling play dough, playing balloon volleyball while sitting, and using an elastic stretch band. This VNA also had a program for Alzheimer's families, free of charge, that included once-a-month visits by a member of the care team. *Where have you been all these years?* I had never before realized that the level of services provided varies among different VNA branches. This branch, I would later learn, was one of the best in the area.

My mother recovered from her hospitalization at home. It was her sixteenth year in her Alzheimer's journey. She walked slowly, shuffling mostly, and needed assistance. Her urinary incontinence was increasing. We often needed to feed her, and her diet had shifted to soft foods like oatmeal, Ensure, and soups. Although she smiled and acknowledged us using facial expressions and nods, we no longer had conversations; she rarely spoke more than a few words. Her balance was unsteady and her falling would likely continue. We purchased a bed alarm and ordered a hospital bed, with sidebars, provided free of charge from Medicare upon a written prescription from Dr. Harmon. The VNA became our ready advisors for resources and medical needs.

* * *

It was Valentine's Day and the telephone rang as I was filling bags of candy for Katie's annual party. The girls would arrive shortly after school.

"Is Jan Simpson there?" Dr. Harmon asked, his Scottish brogue disclosing his identity.

"It's Jan," I said, placing the candy bag on the counter. My mother had just been to the doctor earlier that week for a checkup. Dr.Harmon had disagreed with the Lahey doctors and kept my mother on Coumadin.

"Your mother's Protime was a bit off," he began, noting that the lab test that measured the clotting time of my mother's blood indicated that we needed to adjust the dosing of her medication. I grabbed a pen and wrote down the change, but my antennae were up: something was wrong.

"I want to run more tests on your mother," he said slowly. "I'd like to take some stool samples."

"Stool samples?" I asked. *Ugh.*

"I'll have Sandy send out the test kit. The instructions are inside the package. You'll need to take three samples and bring them to the laboratory."

"What do you think is wrong?" I asked, ignoring my initial disgust.

"She may be bleeding rectally," he said, and my eyebrows shot up. *Huh?* Rectal bleeding was not among the list of things Joan had forewarned me about. "She could have colon cancer." I rubbed my forehead in disbelief.

We continued to talk about the testing required. As the initial shock of the word cancer wore off, I realized that I needed to learn what his game plan was for my mother. I pressed for more details.

"Suppose the test is positive, that she is bleeding, then what? Wouldn't you need to scope her to see what's going on? And then, if you found something, wouldn't she need surgery?"

He replied affirmatively.

"Dr. Harmon," I sighed somewhat exasperated, "Are you honestly going to recommend that we cut her open? She's eighty-two years old with heart disease and Alzheimer's disease. She wouldn't survive surgery." He agreed. "So, why go down this path? Why put her through these tests?" My mother was not going to be poked and probed, not at this stage—she was too frail.

After more discussion, Dr. Harmon and I agreed that we should proceed with the stool samples, to at least confirm that there was, in fact, a problem, but we would unlikely take things any further.

I called Jon to tell him about my mother's medication change. I didn't tell him about the cancer. Next week, after the test kit arrived, I would deal with the stool samples.

"Stool samples," I mumbled, shaking my head and picking up another candy bag to fill. "What's next?"

The following morning the telephone rang. It was eight o'clock and Ron's mother was on the line. She sounded distraught.

"I wanted Ron to know that the EMTs are here and they're working on Dad," she said, starting the conversation midstream. "He's not responding."

Ron was running an errand with Eric, so I called his cell phone. Ron returned his mother's call and then called me back, confirming what I had suspected. Ron's father had passed away.

That afternoon Ron flew down to New York to be with his mother. Eric, Katie, and I drove to her house the following morning.

Ron's father was a Navy veteran of World War II. His military funeral was held at Calverton National Cemetery on Long Island. At the close of the ceremony, two soldiers removed the flag from his casket, folding it into a tight triangular package. A soldier stood before my mother-in-law.

"On behalf of the President of the United States, the Department of Defense, and a grateful Nation, we offer you this flag for the faithful and honorable service of your loved one."

Fifty-two million people died during World War II, including 500,000 Americans who left behind grieving mothers, struggling widows, and lonely children. Sixteen million Americans participated in the war, hundreds of thousands returned home physically disabled, and all returned psychologically changed. Both of my grandmothers had sent three of their four children into battle; Ron's father had served in the Office of Strategic Services in Italy. As I watched my mother-in-law place the flag gently on her lap, slowly smoothing the surface with her gloved hand, I realized how much she and he had endured in their lifetime without complaint.

In recent years, I had begun to think that I had sacrificed my career to help my parents, but this funeral reminded me that I could only begin to comprehend a real sacrifice. Ron's father and his generation knew the true meaning of sacrifice, and they had been good teachers. As we drove away from the cemetery, I felt grateful for having spent the last few years learning from them.

TWENTY-THREE / Housing Choices:
Nursing Homes

MY GUT TOLD ME the time to act was now. I had ignored this feeling before, the year after my father's lung surgery. While my instincts had told me to look into alternative living arrangements, I did not, allowing my father's insistence on living at home to override my better judgment. I had paid dearly for that indecision: I had not had information readily available when his death left my mother in need of a new living arrangement.

"I'm going to look into nursing homes for my mother," I told Ron the following weekend.

"Why?" he asked, lowering the morning newspaper.

"She is dying physically now," I said, reminding him of the call from Dr. Harmon and the prospect of adding colon cancer to her list of ailments. "It is possible that the arrangement we have won't work if she needs active nursing care. Ginny and Jon could find it difficult to keep her at home, or the agency might find it difficult to provide her with care." I was also worried about my nieces. Seeing their grandmother die might be traumatizing, and I knew that my mother wouldn't want that either. It was time to do some homework.

I went online first, searching for guidance on choosing a nursing home. I drew a radius around my house, intending to place my mother close enough that I could visit her daily if necessary.

Hoping to narrow the list of choices to three or four decent nursing homes, I sought counsel from three sources. First I called Concord's Council on Aging and spoke with its director. Like all communities across the country, Concord has an organization that provides health screenings, activities, trips, seminars, and advice to seniors. The director gave me a list of five facilities in the area, noting which were for profit and nonprofit, and which had units for Alzheimer's patients. She also discussed insurance and passed along the names of four elder law attorneys who could provide legal advice about asset protection.

Next, I met with the social worker at my mother's day care center who recommended a semiprivate room for companionship and gave me some tips on how to evaluate a good home. She told me to determine if they accepted MassHealth insurance, the synonym for Medicaid, a key to staying in a nursing home permanently instead of being bumped out once the money runs out. She also advised me to observe the aides, to watch for friendly smiles and courtesy toward patients, and to note if the rooms appeared clean and odor free. Finally, she recommended meeting the top administrator, discovering how long he or she has been in charge, and getting a sense of his or her priorities. Red flags in any of those three areas should make me leery to place my mother there.

My third advisor was a social worker at the VNA. We covered many of the same topics, including financial and legal services, but she also raised the issue of hospice.

"It seems like you're really concerned with end-of-life care," she observed. "You might not even want a nursing home, but hospice care instead. That could be started at home, and then continued in a skilled nursing facility if necessary. We also have a new hospice facility opening this fall that may be an option, too."

I understood the concept of a continuous care community in which an elderly couple might arrive living independently and progress over time through assisted living to skilled nursing care, each transition requiring a change of living quarters. I also knew of stand-alone assisted living facilities, where the transition out to a nursing home was often muddled, some facilities pressing for the change when the residents could no longer feed themselves, others allowing residents to remain long past the time when they needed skilled nursing supervision. But I had assumed that the only remaining choice for my mother was a nursing home. Hospice presented yet another alternative.

Hospice is a special way of caring for a person whose physician has determined that he or she has less than six months to live. Hospice services may be provided at home, in a hospital, or in a nursing home and are paid for by Medicare, Part A. The hospice care team, which includes nurses, social workers, physicians, clergy, and volunteers, all work together, according to the literature she gave me, to "help the patient and the family make the most of each day of life remaining by providing comfort and relief from pain. The goal is comfort, not cure." My mother was approaching the end of her life. Whether she had six months or sixteen months remaining I did not know, but the end was somewhere on the horizon. Now I had another option to explore.

I mentally filed away a plan to look into hospice care and made appointments with three nursing homes that I dubbed the Ritz, the Hyatt, and the Holiday Inn. I decided to evaluate the Ritz first, a continuous care community with a strong reputation. This facility would provide the benchmark of quality against which I could compare the other two homes.

I met with a female administrator who was effusive about a new dementia unit constructed to encourage independence and "failure-free activity" with Alzheimer's residents. In our telephone conversation, I had told her that I suspected that my mother was a candidate for their skilled nursing facility, but she overrode my concern, wanting me to tour the new unit. The fact that it was less than 50 percent occupied probably drove her enthusiasm.

The facility was indeed impressive. There was a warm and spacious common room with natural overhead lighting; an ice cream parlor nestled into a far corner with a full, fifties-style kitchen across the hall; a music room; a library; and even an enclosed outdoor garden. The unit was an exceptional attempt to create a homelike atmosphere for residents whose forgetfulness left them at risk for injury, but who still had cognition to enjoy the news, companionship, and an ice cream with their grandchildren. As we wandered by the kitchen, I peered in at the residents involved in a discussion of current events. They looked my way curiously. I felt a brief wave of sadness, for they appeared as my mother had when my father died, still conversational and physically able. I moved away to avoid interrupting their session, following my guide up the second hallway toward the chapel.

In the deserted hallway, a woman sat in a wheelchair alone. I smiled at her and she returned my gaze slowly with eyes glazed. *Ah, the Haldol haze*, I thought. I was unperturbed by her inability to respond to my smile, but was bothered by the fact that this woman sat alone in the hallway, unattended and unable to wheel herself down to the kitchen to listen to current events. She looked physically able, but she seemed mentally incapable of action, in sharp contrast to her companions whose voices echoed up the hallway.

I shook my head slightly. Nursing homes and psychiatric hospitals have replaced physical restraints with chemical ones. Dementia patients are no longer tied to beds and chairs to prevent wandering—the same effect can be achieved by medication. But the result, a sluggish, zoned-out demeanor, can often mistakenly convince a family that poor old mom or dad is brain dead. I tried to shrug off my discomfort, but it was an effort not to wheel her to the parlor for some ice cream.

I had seen enough. My mother was definitely not eligible for this unit since she would need more physical care. I asked my guide to show me their skilled nursing unit. We took an elevator upstairs where, once again, the impression was one of light, cleanliness, and cheer. I inspected a semiprivate room, wandered past the dining area, and found the common room, where several residents napped in wheelchairs as a pianist played classical music.

One napping woman, hunched over in her wheelchair, caught my eye. *Gosh she's going to have a stiff neck when she wakes up*, I mused. *It's a shame they don't use recliners.* If my mother and father-in-law appeared more able to visitors, perhaps it was because they sat or napped in recliners most of the day.

Our last stop was the business office, where I sat for a few minutes in a waiting area trying to eavesdrop on a conversation between a staff member and an aide who seemed disgruntled about her schedule. The business manager interrupted my snooping, reviewing the admission contract and procedure. This home would cost my mother $300/day, all privately paid, as my question about MassHealth insurance was met dismissively. Like all pricey hotels, I assumed that the final bill would include hidden costs, room taxes, medication fees, and the like, pushing the daily price to $400 or more.

On the ride home I reflected on the facility, glad that I had visited it first. Its reputation for quality was certainly well deserved, for despite my nit-picking, the facility seemed well managed, and the new Alzheimer's unit was a thoughtful attempt to treat dementia patients in a homelike setting. I was not surprised that the unit was half empty, however, for the economics of the disease meant that only a few, truly wealthy families could afford to put their loved ones there. Unlike other illnesses, with short and well-defined trajectories, the duration of Alzheimer's is unpredictable, though twelve years is the standard estimate. Paying nursing home fees between $150,000 and $200,000 per year would bankrupt all but the wealthiest of families. The new Alzheimer's unit was fabulous, I mused, just a poor business model.

I visited the nursing home that I dubbed "The Hyatt" next. The lobby was nondescript, the receptionist sitting behind a lone desk. I was greeted by a male administrator, who brought me to his office for a chat. As we spoke, he filled out a form, capturing my mother's medical history, circulating back repeatedly to her psychotic breaks and wandering. I found his questions annoying and him decidedly unimpressive. He spoke as though he was doing us a favor by taking my mother off my hands. *My mother can't even stand without help, she's hardly going to be a troublemaker.* I smiled and patiently answered his questions, trying to refrain from making a quick judgment about the facility based on my visceral reaction to one administrator.

We began our tour, first through the assisted living facility. The floral wallpaper in the common room seemed cliché and the cavernous room where church services were held reminded me of a grand hall at a nearby Christian retreat. We walked toward the lobby, crossing over the foyer, past a nicely appointed dining room toward the skilled nursing area. There were three wings. He pulled opened the steel doors in the first wing.

The sudden cacophony of color and sound startled me. Wheelchairs jammed the bright pink hallways, edging each other out for space like yellow cabs on the streets of Manhattan. I inhaled and exhaled slowly, trying to control my facial expressions.

I wandered along the hallway ignoring my host, glancing into semiprivate rooms which held two hospital beds. A few residents had tried, unsuccessfully, to make their antiseptic rooms feel inviting, with pictures from home on a bureau. *How can you sleep with these pink walls?* I thought. My eyes met those of a male resident, sitting in his wheelchair in the safety of his private room. I smiled and he returned my smile—he seemed too young to be there.

We walked past a small dining area where a harried aide was helping patients eat, one stretched out on a recliner, mouth agape, toothless. I noticed three women, wheelchairs touching, clustered together and chatting. I smiled at them; they reminded me of my mother and her coffee klatch.

"What are you smiling at?" one woman sneered, her eyes squinting angrily at me.

I hesitated to respond. *I can't tell you that I think you're cute.*

"You wouldn't be smiling if you were sitting here!" she continued, nearly spitting her words at me. My host began talking, trying to distract me from her outburst.

"Oooh," her loud voice followed us up the hallway. "If I could, I'd get up and wipe that smile right off her face!"

I wanted to laugh aloud, for the embarrassment of my pompous guide was priceless. He attributed her rudeness to the nature of some elderly people but I disagreed. Her candor was simply a sign of good mental health: she hadn't given up, she was fighting back, and she was right. It was an awful place, and I was a fool for smiling pleasantly instead of being outraged. I nodded silently at his remarks.

On the ride home, I scratched that home off my list, but I felt a bit sorry for its residents. The facility would benefit from my family's attention. Within a month, Judy would have the walls repainted with soothing décor and colorful accessories. Sundays would bring family parties, with goodies and music: Ginny would bring board games and brainteasers; Walter would provide ice cream frappes all around; and the kids would do their parts too, painting everyone's nails and filling the halls with the least expensive and most effective remedy for aging and death, laughter.

I had one more nursing home to visit, this one located three towns away, outside my preferred driving distance but highly recommended by two of the social workers. I found the buildings nestled near an industrial park, a location which might have been off-putting years before. I had learned from my mother's experience with day care, however, that landscaping and architectural features are not indicators of the commitment of the staff to provide loving, competent care to an elderly person.

I waited on a bench inside the entrance and was greeted within minutes by the director of admissions, whose card indicated that she was a registered nurse. We sat in her office and reviewed my mother's medical history. I explained my mother's home situation and the possible need for nursing home care as the end approached. We discussed her insurance coverage and I noted, as I had with the other nursing homes, that she could self-pay for a year or so, if necessary. Unlike at the Ritz and the Hyatt, the director waved that comment off, pressing that her role included working with families to maximize the use of insurance coverage before dipping into personal funds. Her sincerity was authentic and appreciated.

We toured the facility, which had three units: one for short-term rehabilitation or respite care; a long-term care unit that was small and clean, each room neatly decorated with personal items from home and residents that appeared ambulatory; and a dementia wing that they called the "Special Care Unit" where my mother would be admitted. The director opened the door, and I stepped into the unit, greeted by the pungent odor of soiled diapers.

I glanced into the resident rooms, each resembling a hospital room. One held a bed-ridden patient, the probable source of the aromatic welcome. In the lounge at the end of the hallway, ladies in wheelchairs were arranged in a tight circle, wheel against wheel, surrounding an activities director. They all looked up at me, grinning, as I walked past the one male resident sleeping near the nurses' station. *Well, at least these ladies seem happy.* I left with a folder that included an application form and the resident guidelines. The room rate was $260/day, and the staff included six aides assisting eight to ten patients each.

I was now finished with my tour of three of the best quality nursing homes in the area, grateful that I was under no pressure to choose one and move my mother immediately. Each of the homes had strong features, but none was perfect. Although I would not make any placement without Ginny's input, I now knew one thing for certain: nothing would be better for my mother than her current situation. I resolved to keep her at home for as long as possible, but the timing of my nursing home tour proved foretelling. Two months later, finding my mother's care too taxing physically, Helen quit.

TWENTY-FOUR / Home Care and Hospice

I T WAS JUNE, and Helen's departure had left a gaping hole in support during the week. Unfazed by the daily rate, which was similar to that of the nursing homes I had visited, I decided to fill her place temporarily with aides from the agency. Until now, I had carefully managed my mother's expenses, anticipating reaching the point when her savings would be consumed rapidly for either nursing home fees or skilled home care—we were now at that point. In the fall, I would consider other options.

It would seem the use of one agency in my mother's care would provide a steady flow of support. Instead, the agency, unable or unwilling to assign the specific people we requested, used a number of different aides. Consequently, the quality of care was inconsistent and the enthusiasm of the aides often absent. Ginny and Jon felt the impact most, with Ginny frequently needing to remind the aides about the scope of their assignment that went beyond simply watching our mother and feeding her, but also included doing her laundry and keeping her apartment clean. Ginny's ability to juggle work, teaching, tutoring, teenagers, and our elderly mother made it challenging for her to accept the lackadaisical nature of some aides.

"You would think that sheer boredom would drive them to keep busy," Ginny commented one day. "Instead, they sleep on the couch or lounge around, claiming other work is outside their responsibilities." Ginny often arrived home late in the evening to find Jon handling some minicrisis that an aide had caused: no-shows, flat tires, and poor attitude became part of their daily lives, which were busy enough with jobs and family responsibilities.

One Friday in late August, I stopped by with the children to drop off some supplies for my mother. My mother was at day care, but Willa, her aide, was not at home. Knowing that my mother was increasingly at risk for falls or medical crises, we told the agency that the aides were required to stay in her apartment while she was at day care so that they could handle an emergency if need be. Although we had a busy day ahead, I agreed to let the children stay for a swim in Ginny's pool, wanting to wait for Willa to return so we could chat about her absence.

"Auntie Jan?" my fifteen-year-old niece called out her bedroom window to the pool. I was in a lounge chair, flipping through a magazine. "Nana's day care is on the telephone. They want to talk to my parents, but they're not here."

"I'll take the call," I said, getting up and heading inside. Lori was on the telephone. She expressed concern about my mother's lethargy and her inability to drink fluids. She indicated that she might be dehydrated and suggested that we bring her to the doctor immediately. Lori was not one to panic. *If she says to bring my mother to the doctor today, it must be serious.*

"Is Willa there?" I asked. She wasn't. Annoyed, I left the kids with their cousins and drove to the day care to get my mother, returning to Ginny's before the hospital. I had intended to take my mother to the Lahey Clinic, only a ten-minute drive from the house, but I had hoped to bring Willa along so I would not have to cancel my plans for the day. Willa was still missing, now for nearly three hours since she dropped my mother off that morning.

I packed a bag of snacks and drinks, called Ron to pick up the kids after work, and drove my mother to the Lahey Clinic for saline. On the drive I contacted the agency and explained the situation.

"You know, Annemarie," I said angrily to the director. "We pay for twelve hours of time each week when the aides have nothing to do. Nothing! And all that we ask is that they stay in my mother's apartment in the event of an emergency. Well, here we have a small emergency, something that Willa could have easily handled, and where is she? Who knows! And I don't even have a cell phone number where I can reach her. This is unacceptable!" *Ginny and Jon are saints to put up with this.* "Please find Willa and send her home.

And don't expect my mother to pay for today!"

A few hours later, my mother was hooked up to a bag of saline. She responded almost immediately, smiling gently at my chatter. As we talked, the emergency room doctor came in and asked to speak to me outside.

"I ran several tests while she was here to look for infections," he said. "Her lungs are clear, and there's no evidence of a urinary tract infection." His body language suggested that he was surprised by mother's physical condition.

"Oh, that doesn't surprise me. She's in pretty good shape." I smiled at the doctor. "We only came in for some saline, at the request of her nurse. If they could have provided it at day care, we wouldn't be here." The doctor seemed curious about my mother, though, in no hurry to move on, so I explained her personal history, her living arrangement, and our strategy to keep her active in home care.

"Her physical mobility probably prevents most of the infections you typically see at this stage. In fact, over the past three years, she has been hospitalized for only five nights."

"Five nights?" he repeated, eyes widening.

"Yes," I replied nodding. "She was here for three nights with a touch of pneumonia, and she spent two nights at Mount Auburn a while back because she was shaky and her meds needed to be adjusted." I was silent for a moment. At this stage of Alzheimer's disease, my mother should have been a burden to both the health care system and the taxpayer, yet she barely registered as a blip on the screen. Why? Because our family had absorbed the burdens of her care, and in doing so, also received the benefits of keeping her with us. Over the years I had become bemused by all the hand-wringing among politicos and pundits about rising health care costs and aging baby boomers, for few of their proposed remedies emphasize the least expensive and most obvious solution to the problem: provide high quality, easy-to-access home care services to elders or their caregivers that will allow the elders to remain in their homes or with their families, integrated in their communities, for as long as possible. Ginny and I are typical of the forty-four million American families who currently care for at least one ill elderly relative. Like millions of others, we *wanted* to help our parents and we did all we could to keep our mother out of a nursing home. But the challenges of creating a web of support and finding resources like the VNA, social workers, or attentive home care aides were often overwhelming.

"So far, we've been able to handle her fairly well at home," I continued with the doctor, sensing that my mother had found another ally. "But I'd really like to find a Lahey doctor for her, a gerontologist. She's been treated for twenty years at Mount Auburn, but it's a two- to three-hour excursion to get her there and back. We're starting to have minicrises, and the Lahey Clinic is only a few minutes from her home."

He nodded and offered to make a referral to Dr. Chen, one of the gerontologists at the hospital.

After the meeting, I wheeled my mother across the parking lot, her eyes sparkling as I joked and raced her toward our parked car. To my surprise, Willa was waiting for us at my mother's apartment. She tried to offer excuses for her absence.

"Were you shopping for my mother?" I asked unsmiling.

"No," she replied honestly.

"Are you aware that you are supposed to stay here, in case my mother needs you?" I pressed.

"Yes, but..." I held up my hand to stop her.

"Willa, let me tell you something. Ginny and Jon work full-time. I'm not always around and available. We rely on you to help us take care of our mother. If I hadn't happened to stop by today, my mother would have sat all day at the center, dehydrated, and we would have spent tonight at the hospital with her. That's not right for my mother, nor is it fair to Ginny and Jon."

She seemed unsympathetic.

"Let's be honest," I continued, increasingly annoyed by her attitude. "My mother is not hard to care for, is she? Isn't this one of the easiest assignments you have? She sleeps most of the day and night. I know how easy she is, I care for her on Sundays." She looked hesitant, eyeing me warily. "I also know about some of your other clients, and the nursing home work. That's a lot harder than this assignment." I paused. "Well, you've lost the opportunity to care for my mother. You won't be coming back here again, so please pack up and go home."

She seemed surprised by my anger, for my voice remained calm and even. Upset that I wouldn't allow her to finish her shift, Willa left, my mother napped, and I fixed a cup of tea to wait the three hours until the next caregiver arrived.

If I thought my mother had several years remaining, I might have considered changing agencies or finding another full-time caregiver like Helen. We had been using this agency's services for three years and at this stage, I was reluctant to make a change because of a few bad apples. Instead of spending the fall looking for a new agency, it was time to evaluate hospice.

I made an appointment to visit the Sawtelle Family Hospice House run by the VNA in a neighboring town. I had no expectation that the building would be more than a revamped nursing home, but I was pleasantly surprised when I pulled into the drive. The facility was a restored farmhouse recently converted to a hospice and the exterior, enclosed by a a split-log fence and surrounded by a grassy meadow, was reminiscent of a New England bed-and-breakfast.

The front door opened into a large common room, with a kitchen in the far corner, and as I waited for the director, a volunteer described the quality of care each resident and his or her family received. In addition to round-the-clock medical and nursing care, social workers addressed family issues, chaplains provided religious care, physical and occupational therapists provided pain relief, expressive therapists worked with children, and volunteers, like her, offered companionship and support. Unlike the nursing homes I had visited, it did not seem that the residents were biding time until death, rather, they were actively living out their last days with support services for the entire family.

I was glad that I had waited to explore this option for my mother. The facility was clean, peaceful, and centered on providing optimal comfort for the resident and family. Each of the nine patient rooms had a comfortable sitting area for visitors, and there were three guest rooms available for family members if they wanted to stay overnight. I met with a floor nurse who provided me with some reading materials unlike any I had seen to date. One booklet, entitled *Gone from My Sight*, described the dying experience from a time frame of three months to within minutes, detailing physical and psychological behaviors that included withdrawal, a decreased food intake, disorientation, irregular breathing, and decreased blood pressure. I was also given a worksheet that was used to assess and scale hospice status in an Alzheimer's patient. The assessment confirmed what I had observed anecdotally, that Alzheimer's disease is human development in reverse, a journey back to infancy and birth. The assessment scaled the level of dementia as follows:

7A: Ability to speak is limited to approximately six intelligible words or fewer in the course of an average day or in the course of an intensive interview.

7B: Speech ability is limited to the use of a single intelligible word in an average day or in the course of an interview (the person may repeat the word over and over).

7C: Ambulatory ability is lost (cannot walk without personal assistance).

7D: Cannot sit up without assistance (e.g., patient will fall over if there are not lateral rests [arms] on the chair).

7E: Loss of ability to smile.

7F: Loss of ability to hold up head independently.

My mother was at Stage 7D. In addition, the patient must have all of the following characteristics: unable to ambulate independently, unable to dress without assistance, unable to bathe properly, incontinence of urine and stool, and unable to speak or communicate meaningfully. My mother met all of these criteria.

Finally, the patient must have had one or more of the following medical complications related to dementia in the past year, severe enough to require hospitalization whether or not hospitalization had occurred: aspiration pneumonia, upper urinary tract infection, septicemia, decubitus ulcers (multiple, stage 3-4), fever recurrent after antibiotics, and/or inability or unwillingness to take food or fluids sufficient to sustain life.

After reading the list, I better understood the surprise of the Lahey doctor. My mother's mobility had helped to prevent the infections so commonly found in dementia patients that they were part of the criteria for hospice eligibility. The inability to take food caught my eye as my mother increasingly ate only with much cajoling by her aide or us. It became clear that my mother was hospice eligible.

As I drove away from the farmhouse, I was grateful that we had been able to keep her at home until she reached this stage of need. Hospice care, and not a nursing home, was now her best option. Hospice services could be provided at Ginny's home and, if necessary, continued at the hospice facility. At a price of $150/day, which would be covered by Medicare, this option provided not only a lovely environment in which my mother could spend her last days, but also one that would cost her little to nothing.

TWENTY-FIVE / A Final Birthday

IT WAS A SUNDAY IN LATE OCTOBER. Ginny and Jon were away for the weekend, taking a much-needed break from their hectic routines. After teaching seventeen charming nine year olds songs about the walls of Jericho at Katie's Sunday school class, I drove to my mother's home with Katie in tow. My mother was napping restlessly in her recliner, a stuffed white kitten on her lap.

"Mom," I said loudly, my face inches from hers. She slowly opened her eyes. "Hi Mom," I repeated, smiling broadly. "It's Jan. My daughter Katie and I have come to spend the afternoon with you. In a while, I'll start making us some lunch. I brought homemade soup. Won't that be good?"

"Yes," she replied sleepily, closing her eyes to shoo me away. I stroked her cheek gently, adjusted her afghan, warmed her hands with mine, and headed into Ginny's kitchen to unpack my bags.

Katie settled next to her Nana with a book on the couch, awaiting the return of her cousins from church. I sat at Nana's table, organizing the mail and bills.

"Mom," Katie said, "what's Nana doing?"

I glanced over at my mother. She was talking animatedly in her sleep.

"I think she's dreaming," I said flipping quickly through the stack of unpaid bills.

"She's a little scary," continued Katie, still staring intently at her grandmother.

"Well, Nana doesn't talk much anymore. And the people who help us care for her have stopped chatting with her, thinking that she doesn't understand what they're saying. With no one to talk to, Nana sometimes talks to herself. That's not a bad thing. Maybe she imagines that she's talking to us or to Grandpa. I think it's easier for her to do that than to start or join in a conversation. Come to think of it," I added with a wink, "I catch myself talking aloud sometimes too. I guess we're both a bit loony!" Katie and I giggled and she returned to her book.

As I wrote out a check, my mind wandered to a recent conversation with a girlfriend whose father-in-law had had a stroke.

"It's awful," she had reported. "The family talks about him in front of him as if he isn't even there."

"Yes," I had agreed. "It's one of the saddest things about some illnesses. People think you don't exist because you can't communicate the way you used to. It's really not that different than raising young children."

I had chattered endlessly to my children when they were infants and toddlers to encourage their language development, even though their responses were only unintelligible garbles or a smile. We listened and danced to music, worked with play dough and made puzzles, ran errands and took trips to the park between naps. It was no different with my mother.

I woke her up at one o'clock for lunch. Katie and her nine-year-old cousin had already eaten and were playing outside. I brought my mother to the bathroom, changed her Depend underwear, helped her wash her hands, and brought her into the kitchen. She sat in her Gerry chair, a special recliner that Medicare provided, and I placed soup and her large-handled spoon on the attached tray. I put a second spoon on the tray for me to use.

I turned on an audiotape of the Andrews Sisters and I slid my right hand under my mother's left one, gnarled with arthritis, moving my hand with hers on top to the rhythm of the music.

"Can you hear the music?" I asked loudly. She nodded and smiled.

"Do you remember the Andrews Sisters, Mom?" I continued. "They were before my time, but I love their music." I sang along with the "Beer Barrel Polka." "Roll out the barrel, we'll have a barrel of fun!" My mother smiled and nodded, her hand moving with mine. "If we could," I teased, "I'd get you up dancing. You always loved to dance, didn't you?"

She nodded.

"Well," I continued, "For now, we'll just sing along while we eat."

I took a spoonful of soup on my spoon, and fed her a mouthful, but she began to cough and gag. I rubbed her back. "Oops!" I said, the lilt in my voice masking my concern. "I think we need to thicken it up a bit." I got up and retrieved a can of Thick-It from the cabinet. My mother's inability to swallow easily meant that she was at risk of aspirating her food, sucking it into her lungs where she could choke or it could linger and cause infection. Thin liquids, like soup broth, water, and ginger ale were more difficult to swallow than milkshakes or Ensure. I thickened the soup and tried again.

She ate slowly and I encouraged her to take her time and use her spoon to feed herself. After thirty minutes, she closed her eyes.

"Mom," I said, "Do you want more to eat?" She nodded. "Then open your eyes." I held the spoon in midair, but she kept her eyes closed.

"Mom," I tried again. "I'm not giving you more food until you open your eyes." Finally, her eyes burst open, wide.

"You fox you!" I laughed and she smiled slyly. "I know you aren't sleeping. I want to make sure you don't choke, okay? I need to see that you are paying attention so keep those eyes open if you want to eat." We continued eating, dancing in our seats to the Andrews Sisters.

After nearly an hour, she signaled that she was done eating by again closing her eyes. I brought a pillow for her head, placed another under her right arm for comfort, and slid her stuffed cat, soft and fuzzy, under her hands for warmth and to keep her fingers outstretched.

A few minutes later my daughter slipped quietly into her Nana's apartment.

"Mom," she said. "Aren't we going out shopping today?"

"You bet," I said. "We have to let Nana rest a bit first, but we'll go out soon, at about three thirty, okay?"

"Okay," Katie replied happily. "I brought my wallet."

"Good girl," I said, giving her a hug and kissing her forehead. "Why don't you play a bit more and I'll let you know when we're ready to leave." She agreed and bounced happily out of the room.

When my mother was ready, I called to the girls, who were playing in the basement.

"Nana's coming with us?" my niece asked incredulously.

"Why not?" demanded Katie. My niece just shrugged her shoulders.

As I helped my mother into the front seat of the car, I thought about her relationship with Katie, who sat giggling in the back with her cousin. My mother and Katie had been together for nine years. The arc of Katie's life, moving from dependency to independency, from innocence to awareness, was the mirror opposite of my mother's trajectory, from a life of independence toward dependency and need. Those arcs intercepted the year my father died, evident as I moved daily from assisting Katie with her bath to assisting my mother with her shower.

I marveled at the impact my mother had on Katie. Katie was curious about her Nana, as she was curious about all facets of her life, and as she learned the answers to her questions, she began to understand. Nana was forgetful. Nana loved ice cream. Snowflakes turn to water on a warm tongue. Nana needed naps. Nana played balloon volleyball. Red paint mixed with blue paint creates purple paint. The laws of nature explained, her mind moving with ease from curiosity to understanding to acceptance, acceptance without judgment, without a sense of what was or what should have been. Nana was simply her Nana: loved, understood, accepted, and included in all of our activities. Katie couldn't imagine us going shopping without taking Nana along.

The following morning, I flipped on the computer in my office to reflect on our outing with Nana and our Thursdays together. I turned often to the cheery, incandescent glow of my computer monitor, a companion who never tired of my stories, who gave me the support I needed to surface, confront, and mollify the emotions that threatened at times to unravel me.

This is what I wrote:

This is end-stage Alzheimer's disease. It is not what most doctors or nurses will describe. Most of their experience is with patients in nursing homes. Visit one sometime, look in the dementia ward. You'll see wheelchairs, not recliners. You'll find one aide caring for seven patients, perhaps more on the graveyard shift. Children? Doubtful. Laughter? Unlikely. The smell of baking cookies? Probably not. Let's not blame the nurses or the aides. How well would you do caring for ten-month-old septuplets single-handedly? But it can look like this. This is what Alzheimer's disease can look like when the patient is cared for lovingly, with support, at home.

Lovingly with support, I mused, reflecting on the support we had been providing for my mother, an impossible mix for most families to duplicate. Her care network included Ginny and me, our husbands and six children, and our large extended family. There were skilled physicians, caring nurses, social workers, aides, and therapists, as well as friends who helped with our children, who made us laugh, who prayed for us. We had knit a web of support, one stitch at a time, over weeks and months and years filled with anxiety, frustration, and strain. But through it all we never lost our sense of purpose. My mother gave us that purpose, forcing us each day to reach for a deeper level of compassion in ourselves and to find it in others. I read compassion in the eyes of the doctors who took extra time to help us; I heard it in the voices of the nurses and social workers who gave us advice. Compassion was reflected in the polish Katie and her cousins painted onto their grandmother's fingernails, in my mother's hair washed and combed neatly by an aide, in the cards sent monthly by friends, and in the milkshakes her son brought. I could not have cared for my mother alone, no one could have as her needs were too great. But by knitting together a blanket of care from skilled hands and loving hearts, we were doing the impossible, one day at a time.

The cursor blinked patiently, awaiting the next letter, phrase, or thought. I slid my hands along my face, resting my chin in my palms, staring at the monitor, rereading my words. How often in the past year had I turned to this inhuman companion, like an illicit lover, meeting before dawn or after dark to share secret thoughts, relive life's events, to try to understand, to cope, to remember. I shared stories of my father, laughing anew at his antics and wit. I described the strength of my mother, struggling to walk and eat and live as disease ravaged her brain. I wrote timelines, reflected on relationships, and vented emotions, editing and erasing and evading the truth, as my patient friend blinked, without comment or judgment, awaiting my insights, restoring my balance, understanding the pervasive loneliness of my situation. It had been more than six years since my father had called asking for my help and four years since his death. I had spent more than two thousand days actively supporting two people I loved as they died, slowly.

By now, the early anger that I had felt, anger that nearly destroyed my relationship with my siblings, was gone. Gone too were feelings of guilt that I couldn't do enough for my mother, replaced with the knowledge that we were all doing enough. I had learned to live in the moment, to expect the unexpected, to navigate the world of health care and elder care and to enjoy, truly enjoy, the time spent with my mother. Writing was both therapeutic and a call to action, an outlet for stress and an opportunity for reflection.

I shut off the computer and started to prepare breakfast, comforted in the knowledge that my silent companion stood ready to absorb my anguish as together we walked the final leg of my mother's journey.

*   *   *

"Why are we having a birthday party for Nana? I need to do homework Sunday."

Eric sat at the island in the kitchen eating a plate of scrambled eggs. "It's her birthday, that's why," I replied, admiring his clever excuse. "You can do your homework any other time this weekend."

"But it's stupid!" he persisted. "She won't remember!"

"Oh?" I said, arching my eyebrows. "Tell me, Eric. Tell me about your first birthday party."

"What do you mean?"

"Tell me about the party we had for you when you turned one year old. What do you remember?"

"A lot," he replied defensively.

"Yeah?" I said, my eyes widening in amusement. "Sure you do."

"Well, I remember it from the photos!" he said, realizing where this conversation was headed.

"That's right. You don't remember being *at the party*," I smiled, rolling the last few words for emphasis. "We knew you wouldn't remember your birthday, so why did we bother to have a party? Wasn't that stupid?"

"No," he said slowly. He knew he wasn't going to win this debate. He sighed. "Look," I continued, knowing how much he and his sister had accommodated my mother's needs. "You don't have to spend all of your Sunday there. You can come late, when dinner is ready, have cake, and then leave with Dad." He finished his eggs, agreeing to stay at the party for a little while.

As I watched Eric leave the house to meet up with some friends, I was reminded that his relationship with my mother was significantly different than his sister's. While my mother often joined in Katie's activities, she and Eric had little in common. He was, as my mother once described, "all boy," more interested in his next ball game or the latest news on ESPN than the needs of his elderly grandmother. Yet her presence in his life had an unintended benefit, for as long as my mother was alive, my father never died. He sat on the sidelines at Eric's games, joined us at the dinner table, and joked quietly in those moments before bedtime. Each time I saw my mother, the memory of another long-forgotten story from my father's repertoire was triggered. As a result, I fed Eric a steady diet of my father's stories, full of male humor, to ease the transition from childhood to adolescence, a time when life sometimes seems unfair, especially to a young boy. One such time was when Eric wanted a dog.

"We can't have one," I said firmly, one night at the dinner table, "because he might turn out like Shine." I cast the story line, hoping he'd take the bait.

"Who is Shine?" Eric asked, nibbling on the line as I reeled him in.

"Oh, that was Grandpa's dog. His name was Shine because he had a shiny coat. He was not a very smart dog."

"No?" Eric asked, temporarily forgetting about his request for his own dog.

"No. You know how some dogs chase cats or squirrels or balls?" Eric nodded. "Well, Shine chased cars. Each time a car came down the street, off raced the dog, barking and yelping and trying to bite the front tire."

I watched Eric smile, his mind no doubt creating a cartoon character of Shine racing up the street after cars.

"Yep," I said laconically, "Shine loved to chase cars. And one day," I hesitated just as my father had done years before, "he caught one."

Silence. The edge of my lips curled up slightly, my eyes twinkled, awaiting Eric's reaction. His eyes widened with surprise, his mind filling with the cartoon image of a dog sinking its teeth into the tire of a moving car, flipping around and around as the car rolled by. He burst out laughing.

"Dumb dog," I said, grinning mischievously. "So no, Eric, you may not have a dog. He might turn out like Shine."

Eric played an important role in helping me cope with my mother's decline. It is said that Alzheimer's is the long goodbye as families grieve twice: first, as their loved one slowly loses memory and physical strength, and later, after he or she passes away. I felt this grief profoundly at times, amplified, perhaps, by the earlier loss of my father. It was easy to hide my grief from Ron, with his travel schedule, and from Katie, because of her age, but I could not hide it from Eric. In the weeks, months, and years that we cared for his grandmother, there were days, often Thursdays, when I would feel Eric's small hands rubbing my shoulders, unaware that as I was preparing dinner or washing dishes with him studying in the kitchen, I may have sighed inadvertently or stood staring out the kitchen window, my eyes furrowed, concerned. "Bad day, Mom?" he would ask without expecting any answer. "Yes, Eric, bad day," I'd reply, looking down at him, letting my gloomy feelings rush down the drain with the dirty soapy water.

Today Eric stands 6'5" tall, a three-sport varsity athlete, with an easygoing temperament, an ability to roll with the punches of life, and an ironic wit with a ready smile, no doubt inherited from his grandfather. Eric's quiet support for me, his ability to understand my grief though few words passed between us, had forever shaped his worldview. It heightened his empathetic nature, embedding this athlete with an artist's soul.

So, we held a party for my mother on her birthday. That morning, I packed all of the fixings for a turkey dinner into my van, along with my favorite pots, pans, and serving dishes. After church, Katie and I went to her house to find that my mother had just finished breakfast and was moving to her recliner for a nap.

"Mom," I said, my face inches from hers. "It's Jan. Today is your birthday. Katie and I are here to fix your favorite dinner. I even brought butternut squash. We're going into the kitchen, but we'll be back soon."

"Okay," she said shutting her eyes.

While she slept I prepared dinner. Ginny and her daughters were at church, Jon was sleeping following his late-night shift at the hospital, and Katie sat at the kitchen table with me, snapping green beans. Her assistance ended abruptly when her cousins arrived home, and she hopped down from the table and ran outside to play with her cousins and their new dog. Ginny came in, placing groceries on the table, and moved to the counter to help me prepare the squash.

"Sandra is coming over to see Mom for her birthday," she said. Sandra was a cousin of ours. "Bill and Joanne may stop by, too, they're home this weekend, and Walter, too."

Although I hadn't anticipated that the others would be there, I should have known that my family would never miss an opportunity for a party. I was glad that I had brought a large turkey.

Two hours later, dinner was ready. While Ron carved the turkey, Sandra arrived, and I prepared to serve dinner. I put the food and a stack of plates on the kitchen table and called the children to come and make their plates. As the adults filled theirs, the doorbell rang. It was Bill and Joanne. We found two more chairs and squeezed them around the table. No sooner had they filled their plates with food than the doorbell rang again.

"Hello?" Walter called out, not waiting for someone to greet him at the door. He joined us in the kitchen.

"Gee," Sandra said amused. "They all must have heard the stove buzzer go off."

We ate and chatted about Joanne's high school reunion and the recent marriage of Sandra's son. After a while, I noticed that there was only a bit of butternut squash left, my mother's favorite vegetable. I got up and began to prepare a plate for my mother before the last spoonful was gone.

I went into her apartment alone, gently waking her up. Ron came in behind me offering his help.

"Can we make room for Mom at the table?" I called out over the laughter in the kitchen.

"We'll come in there," Ginny yelled from the kitchen.

Sandra came into my mother's living room and sat on the couch. Joanne followed.

"Hi Mom, it's Joanne. Happy Birthday!"

"Isn't this nice, Mom?" I asked, starting to feed her. "Everyone is here for your birthday." She nodded. "You're eighty-three, imagine that!"

"How do you know that?" my mother asked, in her flat monotone voice.

"Well," I started laughing, always surprised by the way her mind worked. "I remember the year that you were born, and I count from there."

"Yes, Mom," Joanne rejoined, giggling. "Jan was always good at math."

The others wandered into her apartment making introductions as if strangers at a cocktail party.

"Hi, Mom, it's Bill. Happy Birthday."

"Hi, cutie, it's Walter, you look great today." We all sat around chatting as she continued to eat.

"Did you see the chairlift?" Walter asked Bill. That Tuesday we had rented a used chairlift that would carry my mother up from and down into the basement. The aides could now drive into the garage, help my mother step up the single step into the basement, and help her onto the chairlift for a ride to the first floor. My brothers left to give the chair a test-drive and then returned.

My mother remained attentive as she ate her meal, listening intently to Walter's stories, anxiously asking for the ending to his adventurous tale. I smiled, aware that despite Alzheimer's toll on her physical strength and memory, she still hadn't lost her love of a good story.

"Ron," I said quietly, seeing that my mother was still focused. "Let's take some pictures. Sandra, first." I cleared her food and my mother posed with us individually and then in a group, pausing for each snapshot, looking toward the camera when called.

"Now for cake!" I said gaily, and Ron went to the kitchen with Eric and the girls to put the candles on top.

"I didn't get eighty-three candles, Mom," I said, smiling impishly and patting her hand. She looked at me, eyebrows raised.

"Look at her," Joanne laughed. "She's wondering why not? She wants those candles! She has earned every one!" We all laughed.

"Well, I'm sorry," I said apologetically. "I didn't want to start a fire, but we got some that re-light after you blow them out. You can blow them out eighty-three times if you want."

As we waited for the cake, we called the kids back in to help their grandmother open presents. Katie opened our gift first, a fur-trimmed black hat with an attached scarf. I moved my mother's hand along the fur.

"It's soft, isn't it?" I asked and she nodded. "Would you like to try it on?" She nodded again and I put the hat on her head; we all clapped. My mother smiled.

Next her twenty-year-old granddaughter, who a few years before had snatched her wandering grandmother off the street, opened another gift, a warm sweatshirt. Finally, her youngest granddaughter opened a box filled with new slipper socks, hand cream, and cocoa butter. My mother inspected each item.

"Look at the cocoa butter!" I said loudly. "We'll need this next summer, Mom, when we get on our bikinis." She nodded and everyone laughed.

"Watch out! Here I come!" Ron shouted from the kitchen,

entering the room with her birthday cake lit like a fireball. We all burst into song, singing a rousing, if not off-key, rendition of "Happy Birthday." Several more pictures were snapped, and then my mother was served the first slice of chocolate cake. After three mouthfuls, she closed her eyes, weary from the excitement. It had been nearly three hours from her first bite of butternut squash, the longest stretch of time that she had stayed awake and attentive in weeks.

I moved her back to her recliner for a much-deserved nap and we quietly left her apartment whispering. Joanne, Bill, Walter, and Sandra left shortly after they helped clean up the dishes, and Ron took the kids home while I waited for the evening caregiver.

When I arrived back at the house later that night, Ron had just put the kids to bed. I gave him a big hug.

"Thanks for your help today. My mother had a great birthday."

"I know," he smiled. "She really loved it." We were both amazed but not unduly surprised by how she had rallied for the party.

"I am so happy for my mother," I said. "She knew it was her birthday. She knew that we were all there for her." I felt warmth and joy for her lucidity today.

"Before I left," I told Ron, my eyes misting at the thought, "I sat next to her recliner and wished her happy birthday. I told her how fun it was to have Bill and Joanne, Walter, Ginny, Sandra, and the kids all together to celebrate her birthday. I asked her if she had a good day, and, do you know what she said?" A lone tear traced the curve of my cheek. Ron reached over and gently wiped it away.

"She smiled and said, 'A very good day.'"

TWENTY-SIX / The Circle of Care

IT WAS TIME TO RETURN TO WORK. I estimated that my mother's condition would continue to slowly deteriorate and that by September, she would certainly be under hospice care. I initiated contact with a Harvard professor, who graciously offered to help me find a part-time assignment at the business school.

"I feel like a dinosaur," I told Ron after my first interview on campus. "It's been years since I've had to interview for a job. I'm so out of practice!" To my surprise, however, several people expressed an interest in hiring me, one to start immediately, another over the summer.

Spring was coming, and with it came lighter days. Encouraged by the prospect of working again, I felt buoyed, returning from my last interview in high spirits. A telephone message from Lori seemed innocuous enough—she asked me to give her a call, that my mother was having trouble with her bowels. I called her back immediately, but the elder center was closed. After years of retrieving messages of this nature, I did not overreact: if there was real trouble brewing, Ginny would call or Lori would have sounded more concerned.

I arrived at my mother's apartment on Thursday to find her sleeping in her recliner, her caregiver eating breakfast.

"So, how is she doing this week?" I asked her aide as I always did when I arrived.

"Oh, there is no blood today, but on Monday, oh my!"

"Blood?" I asked, at once on edge.

"Yes, when I woke her up on Monday morning, she was lying in blood," she reported almost laconically.

"What?" I could feel the hairs on the back of my neck standing up straight. "How much blood?"

"A lot," she said shaking her head.

"Did you tell Ginny?"

"Yes, of course. Ginny tried to find the telephone number for that new doctor, what's his name, Dr. Chen? But she couldn't find it. So, she told me to take her to the day care so the nurse could examine her."

I was stunned. "And?" I felt like screaming—one might think she was describing mold growing on the bathtub.

"Well, Lori said she would call you."

"Yes, she did but I wasn't home! She didn't indicate that it was serious, so I assumed it was just constipation again. Then what did you do?"

"Tuesday there was less blood," she continued, "and yesterday there was even less. Today she seems okay, only a little." *Thank God we stopped the Coumadin last month or she would have bled to death.*

"I see," I replied, feeling like I was in the midst of some kind of a bad joke. "Is Jon home?" The aide told me he was in the other room, and I found him playing computer games.

"What's going on with my mother?" I inquired, trying to keep the anger out of my voice.

Jon reiterated the aide's story noting that Lori didn't seem to be too disturbed by the blood.

"I see," I said, leaving the den and heading back into the kitchen to place a call to Lori. She was not available, so I left word for her to call me as soon as possible. I placed a call to Dr. Chen's office, getting voicemail. I left a message for Dr. Chen to call me, too.

I gathered up my mother's shopping list and went to the local pharmacy for her medications and supplies. I needed to calm down and think. When I returned, I had a plan.

"Pack up some supplies for her," I told the aide. "We're taking her to see the doctor today."

The doctor still hadn't returned my call. I used my mother's line to call him again. The operator patched me through to the doctor's nurse, where I got voicemail again. I left another message with my cell phone number and redialed the Lahey Clinic to speak with the operator.

"I'm trying to talk with a nurse. My eighty-three-year-old mother is a patient of Dr. Chen's and she awoke on Monday lying in a pool of blood. I've just learned about this today, and I think she needs to be seen by a doctor immediately."

"Let me connect you to triage in the Emergency Room," the operator said kindly. "There is always a nurse on duty there." I waited impatiently for someone to answer the telephone. I got a recording: "Press 1 if this is an emergency...." I slammed down the telephone.

I redialed the operator, and she tried the doctor's office again. The answering machine responded. I left a scathing message.

"This is Jan Simpson, Muriel Albertson's daughter. She is a patient of Dr. Chen's and this is the third message that I am leaving. Please return this call as soon as possible. My mother is bleeding internally. If I don't hear from you by eleven thirty, I'm bringing her to the emergency room."

As soon as I hung up, the telephone rang. It was Lori.

"Lori, tell me what's going on?" I asked abruptly.

"I apologize for leaving a message about bowels on your answering machine," she said, "but I wanted to reach you."

"Yes, you can say whatever you like—it's never a problem. But this seems more serious than you indicated in your message. I'm taking her to see the doctor today, what should I tell him?"

Lori described her symptoms as I grabbed a piece of paper to record her exact words, noting that there was blood consistently throughout the stool. According to Lori, that meant the bleeding was farther up the colon.

"Let's go," I told the aide when I got off the telephone. We drove to the emergency room at the Lahey, my mother pleasantly alert, enjoying our afternoon outing. Just before two o'clock, she was brought into an examining room. A young doctor appeared and I described my mother's medical history, her living arrangement, and noted the earlier suspicion that she might have colon cancer. I reported Lori's words and carefully described the extent to which he should treat her.

"She's here because I don't know what's going on. If she's about to bleed out, then I want her admitted to the hospital. If not, then I want to bring her home."

"Okay," he said. "Let me examine her." He rolled her onto her side. "Could you help?" he inquired, as he pulled on latex gloves.

I stared at him, shocked.

"Well, perhaps her aide," he began, and his voice trailed off. The look on my face gave him his answer. "Erh," he stumbled, ducking the daggers, "or I could get a nurse."

"That's a good idea," I said abruptly. We stepped outside the room, while the doctor and a nurse examined her. A few minutes later, he came out to meet us.

"She's definitely bleeding," he said, stripping off the gloves. "I've ordered some blood tests, and to do more I'll need your permission."

"My mother has advanced Alzheimer's disease. I do not want her poked and prodded unless it's necessary."

"What kind of advanced directives do you have?"

"I have a power of attorney with guardianship and I am her health care proxy. I have been caring for her for seven years. At this stage, we will not make any major interventions, no surgery, and no feeding tubes. She has DNR orders."

"But that only covers respiratory failure," he said. "You'll have to tell us what you want us to do if her blood pressure drops or if she needs a blood transfusion."

"Blood pressure drops? Blood transfusion?" I repeated. I felt like screaming. *Do you see M.D. stamped on my forehead?* I inhaled deeply and glanced at my watch.

"Look," I said hurriedly, "You're going to think that I am crazy, but in forty-five minutes I need to run to a Girl Scout meeting. The meeting ends at five o'clock, and I'll be back then so we can continue this conversation. I'll leave my mother's aide here. If you want to admit my mother, I'll be back to sign the admission papers. If you don't, you should send her home."

I left the hospital and drove Katie and her friends to their Girl Scout meeting. Midway through, my sister called on my cell phone. She told me not to bother returning to the hospital—they were sending Mom home.

Later that evening I called my three oldest siblings and my cousin Sandra.

"Mom is bleeding internally," I told all of them. "Of all the things that could happen to her, this is not what I had anticipated. I think that we're getting close to the end. If you want to see her, you should make plans to do so soon."

Early Friday morning, I called Lori to thank her for examining my mother and to brief her on the emergency room visit.

"Lori," I continued, "If you can believe this, they asked me what I wanted them to do if her blood pressure dropped or if she needed a blood transfusion. I don't have any idea! I didn't have to give them an answer because they sent her home, but that doesn't mean these issues won't surface again. Can you help me understand any of this?" I sat at my daughter's desk, staring absentmindedly out the window at the woods behind our house, the ground a patchwork of snow and mud. "Doesn't your blood pressure drop when you're dying? So, isn't that like the DNR decision? If she's dying, I don't want them to intervene, right?" I did not wait for an answer. "And a blood transfusion, what is that all about?"

Lori explained that if my mother lost enough blood, she could require a blood transfusion. "What was her hemoglobin level?" she asked, noting that a transfusion is typically given when the hemoglobin level drops below seven. I didn't know but I offered to get a copy of the lab report.

"Lori," I said pointedly, "We both know what that doctor was asking me to decide. So, if they bring up the blood pressure again, I'll say to let it go. But with a transfusion, what would you recommend?" The line went silent, and in that moment I realized that she might not be able to answer. I rephrased the question and asked, "If this were your mother, what would you do?"

"I'd give her a transfusion," she said. "The lab data will tell us how much blood she has lost."

I called the Lahey Clinic and asked to speak to the laboratory. To my surprise, a live body answered. I explained my situation, my mother's Alzheimer's disease, and that her nurse wanted a copy of the lab report to manage her follow-up care.

"You are her daughter?" the impervious voice replied. "Well, I can't release information to you." I patiently re-explained my role in my mother's care, that she was bleeding internally, and her nurse needed the lab data from her emergency room visit.

"We don't release medical information without signed authorization from the patient!" she replied haughtily. *Ah, I drew the lucky card this morning. Wouldn't you know I'd get someone who follows all the HIPAA rules protecting medical privacy? I'm sure the medical system will implode if she releases the iron level for one old woman.* I patiently re-explained that my mother was a widow who had advanced Alzheimer's disease and could not sign her name, but that I had legal authorization to access her records.

"I have a health care proxy," I said, growing impatient.

"Well," she said and I could hear the smirk in her voice, "that's not good enough. You need a power of attorney."

"I have that, too." I was losing my patience. "Now, I need that lab report, TODAY! My mother is bleeding internally and her nurse wants the numbers. What would you like me to do? Shall I hand deliver the power of attorney to you right now, or will you accept it by fax? I can be over to your lab in about twenty minutes and I'll be happy to wait until you find the report."

There was silence.

She gave me her fax number. Before hanging up, I told her that I'd be over in two hours if I didn't have the report in hand. I started upstairs to my home office when the doorbell rang. It was Walter.

"Hey, come in, put on the tea, and stay for lunch," I said. "I'll be right down." I faxed the power of attorney to the lab and went downstairs to visit with Walter. He made excuses that he had been nearby looking at property to buy, but I suspected that he just wanted to talk about our mother and my call the previous evening. While we were chatting over sandwiches, I heard the fax go off with my mother's lab report.

The report showed that my mother's red blood cell count, hemoglobin, and hematocrit numbers were below the preferred range, but above the level requiring immediate action. After talking with Lori, I made an appointment for my mother to see

Dr. Chen in two weeks, right after spring break. We were taking Eric and Katie to Florida for five days, the timing of which was a fortuitous opportunity to relax before returning to what was sure to be a stressful spring.

The following Thursday, Rachel, the physical therapist from the VNA came by, giving me a list of suggestions for my mother's care.

"Put washcloths, curled up, in both hands during the day, and slowly open and close her fingers to encourage her flexibility." I wrote her instructions in a notebook. "She's arching her neck," she continued, "so keep a pillow behind her head so her chin faces down while she is sleeping. She shouldn't sleep in a chair with her head back. And do not feed her with her head back, that opens the airway and makes it easy for her to aspirate food." My mother made a rattling noise, and Rachel's eyes met mine.

"That's new," I said, reading her mind. "I was here on Sunday, and she sounded fine. I checked her today for a temperature, but she doesn't have one." Rachel cautioned the aide and me to keep watch for unusual congestion.

"I'm going to bring a pad over next week for her bed," she said. "Her hips and tail bone are most susceptible for bedsores," she continued. "Put extra lotion on her hips, knees, heels, elbows, and ankles. Rub around the bony areas to stimulate blood flow."

When I described the events of the past week, she asked me whether I'd called for a hospice evaluation yet.

"Not yet," I said. "You know, I started asking Ginny to give me a date two months ago because I thought that she or Jon would want to be here. She still hasn't done so, and I'm not sure why. It's not like her to drag her feet." Rachel nodded silently. "I guess that's not unusual, is it?" I asked.

"Would you like me to set up the evaluation?" she offered.

"It really is time, isn't it?" I replied, looking at my mother sleeping in her recliner.

"Yes," she said, "and I can make the arrangements for you."

"No," I said, smiling wanly. "I'll call today and set up an assessment for the week after next." We proceeded to awaken my mother so Rachel could see her walk. My mother smiled pleasantly, forever social, as Rachel touched her arm and chatted.

"Can you walk for me Muriel?" she asked, and my mother walked an unsteady ten steps from her chair toward the bathroom and back to the chair, supported under one arm by her aide. She dropped heavily onto her chair and remained awake as Rachel praised her and showed the aide how to pull her safely to her feet. Watching them, I felt so grateful for the support of my mother's care team from the VNA.

There were no calls on Friday from Lori, which I took as a good sign. I spent much of the day in the laundry room, getting us packed for our week away. That evening, Ron took the kids and me to our favorite local restaurant for dinner. He was in the midst of a business deal and his cell phone rang incessantly.

"Could you shut that thing off while we are eating?" I asked, needing a few minutes of peace. After a quick dinner, Ron drove the kids to the video store while I went home to finish packing. There were four messages on our answering machine.

"Auntie Jan," said my niece "my mom asked me to call to tell you that they rushed Nana to the hospital. She choked at dinner." Beep.

"Hi, it's Annie again, please call my mother on her cell." Beep.

"Jan," this time it was Ginny, "Mom choked on her food. I think she died. They are not bringing her to the Lahey Clinic because the emergency room is diverting patients to other hospitals." Beep.

"There's no one home," a voice said in the distance. Beep.

I erased the messages and called Ginny's cell phone.

"Ginny it's me."

"I think she's gone," Ginny said crying. "I sent her in the ambulance with Lindsey." Lindsey was my twenty-year-old niece.

"Did she have the DNR papers?" I asked.

"Yes," she replied.

"Okay, I'm on my way."

The community hospital where my mother was taken was thirty minutes away. I hung up and quickly called the cell phone of a friend who was spending the weekend with us while searching for a home in the area. He offered to end his night early and stay with the kids so Ron could meet me at the hospital. I ran upstairs to my office and found my mother's original DNR order and her medical fact sheet. I heard the garage door open and the kids chatting excitedly as they entered the house. I caught Ron in the kitchen.

"I have to go to the hospital," I said. Ron's eyes met mine and I shook my head.

"Is everything all right with Nana?" Katie squealed, looking up from their stack of videos.

"I don't know yet," I said, giving her a hug and forcing a glimmer of hope into my voice. "Aunt Ginny is on her way to the hospital, but I need to get there, too. You can watch your movies, and I'll be back as soon as I can."

"Are you sure?" she continued, growing agitated. "I don't want Nana to die!"

"Don't you worry about that," I said. "Nana has been very sick, but I don't know how sick she really is, honey. What movie did you get?" I hoped to distract her. She settled down and went into the den.

"Marvin is on his way back," I told Ron quietly. I gave him directions to the hospital and ran upstairs one last time for the power of attorney. I nearly tripped over Eric sitting at the top of the stairs.

"How bad is it?" he asked, staring blankly down the stairs.

"Pretty bad," I told him. His face fell—he knew his grandmother was dying. He reached out to give me a hug, rubbing my back gently. I gave him a squeeze and ran off.

By the time I arrived at the hospital, my sisters and brother Walter were already there. I found Ginny in the E.R. where she told me the news. My mother was still alive, hooked up to a ventilator.

TWENTY-SEVEN / The End

GINNY AND I STOOD ALONE in a hallway outside the emergency room.

"What happened?" I asked.

"She choked on food at home," she said. "I did the Heimlich maneuver until the ambulance took her away. Lindsey went in the ambulance because I was tutoring a little boy and had to wait for his father. When Mom got here, she was minutes away from dying. They had the DNR orders, but without you here to give the okay, they resuscitated her."

"Wonderful," I replied, shaking my head. I stood silently and let the words sink in. "Tell me exactly what happened."

As she told the story, I pressed her for details. How long after Mom began choking had she started the Heimlich maneuver? How long before the ambulance came?

"Did they give her oxygen in the ambulance?" I needed to know if she had brain damage.

"Yes," she replied. "But the EMTs didn't ventilate her, respecting the DNR order. It was the emergency room doctor who ignored the DNR order and put her on a ventilator."

I went in to see my mother, crowding in next to the others.

We stood around her bed, spilling outside the curtain that encircled it. I held my mother's hand and rubbed her forehead gently. The voices grew silent and one by one, each sibling left until I stood alone beside the bed. A nurse fussed with a machine in the corner of the room and when we were alone, she confirmed Ginny's story and apologized for ignoring the DNR order.

"That's not an issue right now," I said flatly. "What's done is done." I couldn't go there. I shut down. Anger: off. Grief: off. Fear: off. I needed to think, emotionally detached. There would be time later to cry.

"What happens next?" I asked.

She said my mother was awaiting a bed in the intensive care unit.

Ron arrived, standing near a nurses' station. As my siblings milled about, we began to quietly discuss next steps.

"I say take her off the machine," my sister Carol said.

"Me too," said Walter. Ginny agreed. Stunned by their decisiveness, I said nothing.

While we rotated between the waiting room and her bedside, Ron gently pulled me aside.

"Look, I know how you make decisions," he said quietly. "You don't like to be rushed, and I just want you to remember that you're in charge. It's only what you think that matters. Your parents made that choice for a reason. Don't forget it."

"But they all want to pull the plug," I said. "I can't believe how easily they can say that."

"That's because it's not really their choice," he said. "Look, you don't need to decide anything right now. She's not going anywhere."

"Yeah," I continued, "but at some point I do need to make a decision. I just need time to think. I'm going to call Bill. He needs to be here."

"He didn't seem to need to be at your father's side," Ron said, referring to Bill's absence at my father's passing.

"This is different," I said. "He is her oldest child, her oldest son. I don't have to tell you how special the relationship is between the oldest son and a mother, do I?" He nodded knowingly.

The young attending physician came over and introduced himself. He was heading off shift and seemed almost cavalier, perhaps delighted to get off at seven o'clock on a Friday night. *Do you have any idea what you have just done?* I let Ron do the talking, knowing I might lose control. The doctor confirmed what Ron had said.

"You don't need to decide anything right now," he said. "They will be taking her to the ICU."

I found a quiet corner and called my brother Bill who was at home in New York. He, too, thought we should wait.

"But Bill," I said, rubbing my forehead, "please, let's talk about this. You and I make decisions the same way—we like data, we take time. This might be a blessing in disguise for Mom because she is not going to get any better. I know that she is at the end of her physical life. She is bleeding internally. She's lost her swallowing reflex. We decided long ago against feeding tubes. This has never been about the Alzheimer's—I don't care if she is mentally impaired. It is about her being at the physical end of her life." We talked, and eventually we agreed: she should come off the ventilator.

"Come. We'll wait for you to get here."

There were too many of us standing around in the emergency room so we found an empty waiting area just outside the E.R. and spread out among the chairs. Sandra and her husband had joined us, along with Walter's wife, Judy, and Carol's husband, Steve. Jon took orders for coffee and left the hospital grounds for an all-night coffee shop nearby. To pass the time, Ginny recounted the night's events.

"I had just started tutoring a new boy," she said. "We were working on writing a paragraph—you know, topic sentence, three supporting facts, good transitions." We all nodded. "All of a sudden, I heard yelling coming from Mom's apartment. 'Not on my shift! Not on my shift!' Emily, her aide, was screaming at the top of her lungs."

"Not on my shift?" Walter asked, and Carol started giggling.

"Oh my God," I said, "I'm so glad we pay for competence."

"Oh," Ginny said, just getting started. "It gets better!"

"So," she continued, now with a rapt audience, "I yanked opened the door between the study and Mom's apartment, and there is poor Mom, frothing at the mouth, choking, and Emily is standing in the corner, in hysterics, screaming!"

"Jesus," Ron said, shaking his head.

"So, what did you do?" Judy asked.

"I ran into the kitchen for the telephone, but wouldn't you know it? Annie had it in her bedroom! I raced down the hall, grabbed the telephone out of her hands, and dialed 911. Just at that moment,

Lindsey walked in from work, so I gave her the phone, told Annie to sit with the boy, and raced back to start the Heimlich maneuver on Mom."

"I got Mom out of her chair and on to the floor so I could work on her," Ginny continued, "but Emily was screaming so loudly, Lindsey had to go into the kitchen to hear the 911 operator, shouting out instructions to me!"

"Oh my God," Carol said.

"Ginny," Judy said, "only you could be so cool, calm, and collected." We all couldn't help but laugh.

"Well," Ginny said, between the laughter, "the EMTs were there in minutes. They whisked into the house, moved the kitchen table to the side, popped Mom onto the gurney, and out they went with Lindsey at her side!"

"With the DNR orders," I added, gloomily.

"Yep," she nodded, "we grabbed the paperwork and out Mom went."

"By now," Ginny continued, not letting the mood grow somber, "my heart is pounding, and there is Emily, still in the corner and still screeching!" We all burst into loud guffaws. "So, I'm the one with the mother choking, the one who is trying to save her, and there I am patting Emily's arm, saying 'Honey, calm down, calm down. Why don't you fix yourself a cup of tea?'" We were rolling with laughter now, tears streaming down our cheeks.

"Well, we straightened up the kitchen," she said, "and just a minute or two before my student's dad arrived, I sat back down with my young pal. He wrote one heck of a paragraph." We roared hysterically. "When his dad came in, the house was quiet, just as it was when he left."

"Can you imagine what he told his father?" Judy rejoined, still laughing. "I'm sure he said, 'Dad, you won't believe what just happened.'"

"Yep," Sandra laughed. "And I bet he was sent to bed early for telling a whopper." We all nodded in response, still giggling.

Thank God for laughter. I was glad that we were alone in the waiting room—our hilarity would seem inappropriate and callous to anyone who didn't know us. But if you looked past our humor, you would see that our hearts were breaking. Our mother was dying. Through laughter, we were simply bracing ourselves, collectively, for what was to come.

We removed my mother from the ventilator that evening and arranged for family shifts to stay with her continually through the night. I left the hospital around three o'clock in the morning, returning at nine o'clock to find her stationed in a private room on a medical ward. I interrupted my brother Walter, who was chatting to her sedated body in the empty room.

"Have you seen the doctor yet?" I asked, appreciating his gesture, knowing that hearing is often the last sense to go.

"Not yet," he replied, and I opened my canvas tote bag, retrieving the morning newspaper. By ten o'clock, the others had wandered in, jamming every corner of the small room. We found extra chairs, and my nieces sat on the floor. All morning we kept vigil. Ginny graded term papers, Carol worked on embroidery, Jon read one newspaper after another, and Walter filled the time with humorous stories. One niece, dressed in teenage garb complete with hoop earrings, a tank top, and low rider jeans, sought tips on a scarf she was knitting.

"Now this is not your grandmother's knitting circle!" I joked.

My mother slept, attached to oxygen, saline, and a morphine drip, set to 1 cc in a locked box to prevent tampering. At one o'clock, hunger drove most of the group to the cafeteria for lunch, leaving me alone with Jon and my mother.

"Your kids are so amazing," I said, praising them for spending the day with their grandmother.

"This is where they're supposed to be," he said, dismissing my comments. I looked over at my mother sleeping.

"I'm really confused," I said, my brain sluggish and slow. "She came in here within inches of dying, her lungs are full of garbage, and yet her vital signs are good. Something isn't right," I mused. "They're doing something to sustain her." I shook my head, as if shaking loose the cobwebs woven by the strain and sadness.

"Do you know what's going on here, Jon?" I said, too tired to be angry. "I think they're just getting her stable so they can ship her to a nursing home. They don't want her to die on their watch." Jon didn't share my skepticism, but I continued unappeased. "That has got to be it. How do you explain ignoring the DNR order? How do you explain this?" I asked again, gesturing toward my mother. "They want to ship her out, to let her die in a home." *How can I let that happen?*

"Jan," Jon said, patiently, sensing my anxiety. "She's not going to a nursing home. If they want to discharge her, she's coming home with us."

"No, Jon," I said emphatically. "I cannot let you do that. You and Ginny have done enough. That's beyond what's expected."

"Jan," he reiterated. "She will come home with us. I don't like nursing homes. People should die in their own homes." I stared silently at him, this gentle bear of a man. Of all the people in our family, Jon was my mother's guardian angel. He put up with the ongoing disruption of his household; listened patiently day in and day out to the aides; cajoled his daughters through their teen years; corralled Ginny's ambition; and fundamentally, decently, and determinedly made sure that his mother-in-law was properly cared for. But this was not acceptable.

"Jon," I said quietly. "I know that you and Ginny can handle the end, but think about your children. I wouldn't want my own kids to witness that, yours shouldn't either."

"Jan," he said, his deep baritone voice resonant and strong, "how else will they learn to deal with death? They will handle it however they need to handle it. Your mother will be coming home with us, if they release her."

I looked away in gratitude.

All afternoon we kept vigil, the nurses appearing periodically as my mother roused, to give her a shot of morphine.

"What are you doing?" I asked, as they noted that she could get one extra cc of morphine every two hours, if needed. "Why don't you just up the dosing in the IV to 2 ccs?"

"These were the doctor's orders," they replied kindly, and I shook my head in annoyance. *Where is the doctor?*

We waited, organizing another overnight vigil for Saturday night. Ron came by that evening to drive me home, concerned about me driving while so exhausted. There was still no sign of the doctor. My mother awakened, moaning in rhythm with each exhaled breath. The nurses had given us a bowl of water and a small green sponge atop a lollipop stick to use to give my mother water. I watched Ginny swab her parched lips and the insides of her mouth. My mother sucked on the sponge, eyes closed, like a nestling taking a worm from its mother. *I can't stand this,* I thought.

"She seems too alert," I said to Jon quietly, seated next to him on a chair. "Am I right?" Jon nodded affirmatively. I stood and gently rubbed my mother's forehead.

"Mom," I said loudly. "It's Jan. We're all here."

She moaned in acknowledgment, keeping her eyes shut. *Oh my God, this isn't right. This must be so painful.*

"I'll take care of you," I said loudly. "I know that you must be feeling some pain. It'll be alright, I promise." I left her room and went to the nurses' station.

"I want to talk to the doctor," I said sternly. "My mother is too alert. This business of sticking her with needles has got to end! Her morphine needs to be upped so she does not feel pain." The nurses agreed, and one came into her room to give her another shot.

"What's that blood?" someone shouted as the nurse turned to leave.

"Blood?" we chorused, and I noticed blood oozing from the end of the intravenous tubing. The nurse ushered us out of the room and got help to move the IV to another vein, changing my mother's blood-stained clothing and sheets.

"I think her vein collapsed," Ron said quietly as we waited in the hallway. He saw the look on my face.

"I can't do much with everyone here," I said softly. "But this has got to stop. I promised myself that she would never suffer. I'll work with the nurses when everyone leaves." He nodded silently.

"Do try to get some sleep, Jan," he said, rubbing my arm.

Bill and Joanne arrived for the third-shift vigil. We dimmed the lights in my mother's room and I headed to the nurses' station. Initially, my mother's nurse did not instill much confidence, keeping her eyes lowered as I recounted the ignored DNR order, the inadequate morphine level, and my as yet unfilled request to speak to her doctor.

"I have a call into him," she said, not meeting my gaze. Our conversation was interrupted by his call, and I listened as she requested an order to increase my mother's morphine.

"Many doctors give an order that allows for a range of dosing, from 1 to 5 ccs," she said, and nodded in response to the doctor's words over the phone.

"So?" I asked as she hung up the telephone.

"He has increased her dosing to 2 ccs," she said, "and he said to call in a couple of hours if that didn't seem sufficient." It was already after eleven o'clock. I shook my head, but before I could speak she continued. "Well, he would have had a better night's sleep if he had given us more leeway, now wouldn't he have?" She smiled, quickly looking away and shuffling some papers. *Thank God for competent nurses.* I knew my mother was in good hands.

I placed a stiff-backed chair in the corner of my mother's room and collapsed my long frame around it, resting my head on the two-inch window ledge overlooking the darkened visitor's parking lot. While Bill and Joanne worked quietly on a crossword puzzle using the light from the hallway, I tried to doze. My sleep was fitful, though, interrupted once by a nurse offering carrot cake and coffee, and intermittently as my head rolled off the ledge, asleep, to snap suddenly awake. At two o'clock in the morning, a nurse touched me gently, whispering, "The doctor just approved an increase of her morphine to 3 ccs." I sleepily nodded thanks and readjusted my head, my forearms numb and tingling, and my neck stiff and achy. I slept like a snake on a pole, trying not to slip off, until a hazy dawn broke.

I found my mother was sleeping peacefully in her bed.

"I'm going home for a shower," I told Bill and Joanne. "I'll be back in a few hours. Tell whoever replaces you that I want to speak to the doctor today. If he comes by when I'm not here, pin him down to a time when I can reach him." I went home, slept for a couple of hours, and returned close to noon. The doctor assigned to my mother's case had not yet done rounds.

My mother's room was filled again, each of us more subdued than the previous day. My mouth tasted like dusty cotton balls and my head ached. We waited for the doctor, expectantly, and quietly organized our vigil for the workweek ahead. Just after noon, the doctor arrived, hesitating in the doorway, not expecting such a large crowd. He introduced himself and then stood at the foot of my mother's bed.

"I gave orders to increase her morphine last evening," he began, as if that gesture would erase our annoyance at his absence and the needle pricks he had ordered the day before. *Thanks for that,* I thought sarcastically, knowing it was the nurses who had pressed for the medication. I got right to the point.

"You do know that my mother arrived in the emergency room with DNR orders that were ignored," I said curtly.

"Yes, I know," he said, and laughed nervously. I didn't dare look across the room at my sisters' faces.

"She has end-stage Alzheimer's disease," I continued, "and we have taken care of her at home for years. She is now bleeding internally and she has lost her swallowing reflex." I continued to talk, assuming that he knew nothing about her case and hoping to discuss her options despite the awkwardness of doing so with an audience. He was evasive, choosing doctor-speak to avoid giving direct answers. He noted the strength of her heart.

"She has a pacemaker," I said, dismissing his evasion. *She's at the end of her life. Own it, please!* I asked about the range of morphine dosing, an approach the nurse had mentioned that some doctors allow. He avoided a direct answer, noting the constraints of choice in a hospital setting, citing the flexibility available to patients under hospice care. *You are copping out. This is your mistake and my mother will not pay a price for that.*

"What if we remove the oxygen and the saline?" I offered, trying to understand her options. He stared at me silently. I bit the inside of my lip. *Is that it?* I wondered, surprised by his silence. His eyes bore into me. I sighed slowly.

"I just don't want her to suffer," I said, my voice quaking as I tried to hold back tears. *I know that I have to say this because you won't own this decision. But you have no idea how hard this is.* He left her room without saying another word.

"Oh, did you hear him laugh when you mentioned the DNR order?" my sister Carol cried. "I wanted to slap him!"

"He was nervous," Jon replied. "He's not Mom's regular doctor. He doesn't know us from Adam. You should see how many times people say to remove a ventilator and then change their minds."

"They make you say it," I said quietly. "They make you say that it's okay to let someone you love die. They have no idea what they're doing to the family who has to make that choice."

I walked to the window and stared vacantly at the trees lining the edge of the parking lot. It was raining, a gray day, and I inhaled slowly. I returned to my seat just as the doctor walked by in the hallway. He caught my eye.

"It's all set," he said. He didn't bother to step inside her room.

The day nurse entered the room, squeezing by my sisters toward the top of the bed. She shut off the oxygen and gently removed the tubing from my mother's nose. She left the room, and I stood to the left of my mother, gently stroking her forehead. The nurse reached up on her right side toward the saline.

"Is this what you want?" she asked, hesitating for a brief moment.

"Yes," I said, staring down at my mother's face. I couldn't look away. "Do you need for me to sign anything?"

"No," she said, "that's not necessary." She removed the tubing. She left the room and a moment later returned with blankets.

"Could you tell us what to expect?" Jon asked. The nurse described the dying process, noting that her hands and feet would grow cold because circulation to the extremities slows as the body tries to provide oxygen to the vital organs.

"Her breathing will slow down," she continued. "There will be long pauses between breaths, and eventually, her breathing will simply stop." We nodded silently. My mother slept peacefully.

Later that afternoon, Ginny and I were alone in the hospital room, each holding one of my mother's hands. In the silence, my mind wandered back to the first year I returned to Boston, with a toddler and infant in tow, returning to the welcoming arms of my parents. While I juggled consulting contracts and babysitters, soccer schedules and preschool, my parents awaited our unplanned visits, always ready to nourish their daughter and grandchildren with laughter and goodies, cribbage games, and cups of tea. I thought about the photos in frames scattered throughout our home and the hundreds of others unframed that would forever fill our heads with memories and our hearts with the security of having known unconditional love. My children's faces floated before my eyes as I thought about them and their friends, eagerly accepting Nana's lemon drops and another trip for ice cream, and their gentleness and patience that grew as my mother's ability declined.

I reached up and stroked my mother's brow lightly, remembering the year my father died, and how we had tried to distract her so she would not miss his presence. An image of her seated in the stands at a hockey game floated before me, she wrapped tightly in a woolen blanket, her favorite crocheted hat poking above her tiny face. I recalled the parent who walked her arm-in-arm to our car, surely knowing that my mother would not remember her kind words, but might remember the feeling of being wanted and welcomed.

I adjusted the edge of her blanket, taking her cold hand between my warm ones. I remembered that my life in those early days was hectic and harried, like the tic-tic-tic of an egg timer. I rushed from project to playground, to ball field and dance lesson, maddened at first by the slow pendulum of my mother's life, like a grandfather's clock, tick-swing-tock-swing-tick-swing-tock. I had squeezed her appointments and needs into my schedule, blocking time for her as I blocked time for others, just one more task to do, another ball to juggle. But then, slowly, I began to look forward to those Thursdays with her, those five or six uninterrupted hours with no phone calls to answer, no e-mails to read, just my mother and me, shopping or eating or visiting the doctors. I don't know when the change happened, when my time with my mother was no longer a burden but a blessing, but at some point during those Thursdays together, I began to question time, and my lack of it, and my children's time, and how they were spending it, and I began to cut things out, to cut back, to free up time, to stop racing through my life and rushing my children through theirs.

I had always thought my mother was a simple, uncomplicated person, content to be with family and friends. I came to see that she led not a simple life, but a simplified one, with uncluttered closets and an uncluttered schedule. She invested her time in her family, not in a career, building a portfolio of friends, not mutual funds. And though she was now nearly penniless, I considered her a wealthy woman.

As I looked over at Ginny's tear-stained face, I realized that my mother was like women in all communities across the globe, do-ing what is needed and often unappreciated to raise families, sup-port friends, and strengthen communities. When my mother had a toddler and an infant, she too had moved home, into her parents' house, as her husband headed toward the Pacific to fight a world war, with her brothers serving in Europe and her sister in the Navy. And although my mother's joy for their safe return was later over-shadowed by grief at the loss of her young sister, she nevertheless raised the five of us with tenderness and laughter. Each night, long after we were grown and able to live without her support, she con-tinued to kneel beside her bed to say prayers—prayers not for her own needs but for the needs of others.

My mother's breathing continued to slow, with two quick puffs and a long silence. Ginny's eyes met mine, and we nodded.

I thought about her girlfriend Ruth, who said how lucky my mother was to have us, two daughters, with a few university de-grees in our pockets and a few dollars in our wallets, unable and unwilling to leave her alone throughout her final years. Two sisters, fortunate to marry family-centered men, raising family-centered children who pitched in, helped out, and made choices, however inconvenient at times, to support their grandmother. Two women, not unlike our mother, who did our best, tried to stay strong, to keep the faith and stick together, knowing that things somehow would work out okay. "No, Ruth," I had said, finally appreciating the role model we had, "it is we who are the lucky ones."

The room filled once again with our family as my mother's breathing grew more irregular. She rested peacefully, looked serene, her work on Earth now finished.

My mother died at 5:15 p.m. It was the first day of spring.

The Author's Guidance

The last two or three years of a parent's life can be the most poignant, as he or she becomes increasingly frail and you realize that you are on the verge of becoming the oldest generation in your family. I encourage you to actively support your parents along their journey.

Here are some issues for you to consider:

• Housing Choices

Economics, geography, and the family dynamics will determine where your parents live during their last years. It is best to have made some plans before a crisis forces the decision. If a parent has moved in with you or with another family member, you will need to create a web of support that may include family, home aides, visiting nurses, social workers, and other health care providers. If they reside elsewhere, such as in a skilled nursing home, your involvement may still be required to ensure that their needs are being met. It always surprises people to learn that less than 5 percent of all elders between the ages of seventy-five and eighty-five will live permanently in a nursing home, and that only 20 percent of those aged eighty-five and older will do so. Do some advanced planning and be prepared to find and fund home care support.

• Hospice Care

With services funded by Medicare, one would think that more elders would use hospice care. In practice, it is difficult for family members to admit that their loved one is dying and within six months of death. It is also difficult for some elders to be willing to stop the medical interventions that an impartial advisor such as a family physician knows will not prolong life and may prolong suffering. This is where a team of advisors—nurses, a family physician, a religious leader—could be helpful. The six-month rule is not a deadline; if a loved one lives beyond the six months, hospice care continues.

• Your Parents' Legacy

How do you want your children to remember your parents? Are you encouraging them to spend time together? A housebound grandparent provides an opportunity for grandchildren to learn about their grandparents' lives, to sift through those old photos and records, to document their lives. Take videos, prepare scrapbooks, record stories. Encourage that connection, and spend some of your time with them, too. After they are gone, you may regret not learning more about their lives.

• Longevity, What Works

While it is easy to focus on hospitals and nursing care, it is wise to remember that longevity is tied to genetics, nutrition, mobility, social connection, and humor, my proxy for strong mental health. The last years of life do not need to be colorless and boring. Ensuring that your parents continue to be nourished; mobile; engaged in tasks they enjoy such as card games, reading, or gardening; and surrounded by good-humored people will add months, if not years, to their lives.

• Withholding Treatment vs. Withholding Care

Cancer, heart disease, dementia, arthritis, diabetes, depression. Old people live with many diseases, so it becomes necessary to prioritize what treatment is helpful to maintain a high quality of life and what is unnecessary or potentially harmful. At age seventy-eight, chemotherapy for my father following his lung surgery, a treatment that would not increase his longevity, would have meant spending the last two years of his life vomiting and suffering from its side effects rather than playing cribbage with his grandchildren. Surgery for my mother at age eighty-two to address colon cancer would have rendered her immobile, and that alone would have worsened her physical health. There is a difference between withholding treatment and withholding care. As a rule of thumb, I decided that any treatment that was not physically invasive, such as taking medication, getting an x-ray, or drawing blood, was okay, while aggressive intervention, such as surgery, endoscopic treatment, or radiation/chemotherapy was not, unless the physician could justify the outcome. Instead, we focused on providing the best home care we could provide, including good food, good stories, and good companionship.

• Use this Book

Parents resist change. Siblings are distracted by work and family. If you are concerned that your parents are not preparing for their future, give them a copy of this book and, over tea or something stronger, say,

> "Pretend you are Muriel. How would you like your life to unfold if you were not able to make decisions, sign your name, or interact with doctors?" or

> "Step into Bob's shoes. He was sure that lung cancer was a death sentence and took some steps to care for his wife after he was gone. How would you like Mom to live after you are gone?"

Do not avoid the difficult conversations, and if your parents resist, suggest that you are asking because you want them to have control over what happens.

Consider your siblings and their role in the future. Send them all a copy of this book. Then, invite them over for dinner and use the discussion questions that follow to highlight issues that need to be addressed. Decide together on roles and responsibilities. It is better to surface disagreements before your parents' needs escalate so you can find solutions that everyone can live with.

• Next Steps

It is impossible to address all issues about aging parents in one book. Join me and others who are supporting their elderly parents online at www.dontgiveuponthem.com.

Epilogue

I T HAS BEEN SIX YEARS SINCE MY MOTHER'S PASSING. Ron still travels weekly; Eric and Katie are in college and high school, respectively. During the first September without my mother, I accepted a temporary position on the admissions board at Harvard Business School, welcoming the opportunity to meet, interview, and select candidates from a distinguished pool of applicants. It was a pleasure to work on the campus and interact with the students, a few of whom will be among the next generation of world leaders, and each of whom will make a significant impact on their companies and communities. The infusion of their enthusiasm and optimism was the perfect antidote to a decade of elder care, and a much-needed transition back to the world I left behind.

Last April, I launched *Circle of Life Partners* to provide a trustworthy resource for clients navigating significant life transitions. Our first challenge is to help families successfully support aging parents. It is a daunting task, but one that inspires us, knowing that we can have a positive impact on so many lives.

My extended family continues to gather together routinely. Ginny is now grandmother to a darling little girl, who would have been my mother's fifteenth great-grandchild. Ginny surveyed the family for a new name for grandmother—the word "Nana," long the preferred family name, now connotes visions of dementia and forgetfulness. It became an ongoing joke among us as we learned how to say grandmother in many languages. Ginny is now called "Yaya."

I hope that by sharing our story, we may help other families better support their elderly parents through their final years. I didn't know much at the start, similar to parenting my first child, but I have found common themes in conversations with my friends. Those themes and the lessons we learned are built into this story. I'd like to tell you that these years were mostly easy ones, but they were not. Caring for a loved one who is terminally or chronically ill is like sleep deprivation from taking care of a colicky infant or time spent in a war zone—there were moments, at times, simply to be endured. Mary Pipher, noted author and psychotherapist, has observed that being involved in the last years of our parents' lives gives adult children an opportunity for personal development. Frankly, I thought my last growth spurt ended in puberty, or, perhaps, upon becoming a mother. But Pipher is right. Caring for my parents forced me to revisit many facets of my life and shake hands with my own mortality. My perspective is forever transformed.

The disturbing memories that linger from these years are the faces of the elders we met along the journey, like the female patient at McLean Hospital who wanted Ginny to add an extra bedroom for her. "Money is no object," she had said, telling us that no one in her family wanted to help her, despite her affluence, which could have eased the burden. Or the woman who yelled at me in the hallway, reminding me how awful life was in the nursing home. Or the wistful smile of a male patient nearby, sitting in a wheelchair, alone in his private room, looking for companionship. These are the memories that disturb me most, the ones that compelled me to finish this book. The real tragedy of aging is not disease or disability, but of being alone. If our story helps a few more families build a better web of support for their parents, I will consider the effort worthwhile.

My mother died on a rainy, spring day but the day of her funeral was bright and fragrant, with bursting spring colors dotting the route to the church. Following the service, I stood apart from the crowd, overcome with grief. Pete Stanton, my parents' neighbor, approached me and inquired how long my father had been dead. "Well, Jan," he said in his gravelly voice, "just think, he got four years of peace and quiet. It's all over now!" We both laughed as was his intent, the best antidote to tears. My mother's funeral reception was held at my home, where following a rather sedate luncheon, her grandchildren and their children turned on our player piano and began to sing and form a conga line, dancing to Elvis. Somewhere, I know my mother was joining in, tapping her foot, nodding her head in approval.

This journey with my parents began with a telephone call, a call from my father asking for help in a voice laced with worry and regret. He worried about my mother and how she would fare without him and yet his tone was filled with regret, regret that he needed to ask for my support. After all, he was a fiercely independent man, whose long-standing advice to me was, "If you want a helping hand, look at the end of your own wrist." What would your parents do in his place? How will they respond as they enter the last years of their lives? Unlike mine, they may not ask for your help, they may not want help, and they may initially resist offers of support. But unless they are one of the fortunate few who will live well into their nineties and die peacefully in their sleep, they *will* need help. They will need your time, your energy, your affection, your patience, and your laughter as they navigate the treacherous waters of disease and disability. "Don't give up on me," my father had said as he was being whisked away for lung surgery on that day now long ago. We didn't, and that made all the difference.

Lessons Learned

E MBEDDED IN *Don't Give Up on Me!* are dozens of lessons my family learned about supporting our aging parents. While each family situation is unique, what follows are a few of the insights we gained from handling the medical, legal, financial, and caregiving issues that arose as we coped with serious illnesses and the lifestyle changes that accompany aging. I encourage you to reread the book, reflect upon your own family circumstances, and take a few steps toward helping your parents anticipate and plan for their future.

As you embark on this journey with your parents, remember:

You are not alone. Today, there are forty-four million American families caring for at least one elderly relative.

You make a difference. Whether you live in a neighboring town or another country, your support will impact how well your parents live through their last years.

You can't do it alone. Reach out, find help, and create a web of support that will respond to your parents' needs.

Lessons Learned: MEDICAL

❖ **Establish a relationship with one doctor** who will serve as a link to specialists. Recognize that all physicians have limits to their medical knowledge; ask questions and cross-check information using other physicians, nurses, and health care professionals.

∴ **There are two medical systems in America,** a legacy from the days when diseases of the body and mind were treated separately. If your parent takes medication for anxiety, depression, insomnia, or dementia, consider including a geriatric psychiatrist in the mix of specialists.

∴ **Quality of care depends on the family, not the physician.** You can significantly enhance medical care if you or your parents:

- *Create a medical fact sheet* to give to each medical contact.

- *Keep a medical diary* to recall specifics.

- *Prepare for each medical appointment*—open each appointment with the phrase, "The last time we were here..."

- *Research diseases*—write down questions and find answers.

- *Seek out advice from nurses* and other health care professionals.

- *Ensure that friends or family visit during hospital stays.*

∴ **Physicians do not make end-of-life decisions, you do.** Be prepared.

∴ **Watch medications—all prescription drugs have side effects, and proper dosing is vital.** If your parent takes more than two or three drugs, beware of drug-drug interactions.

∴ **Good nutrition equates to good health.** A poor diet can weaken an elder quickly.

∴ **The best medicine is LAUGHTER.**

Lessons Learned: LEGAL

❖ **Wills take care of heirs, not parents.**

❖ **Well-crafted legal documents can prevent family discord.**

❖ **Work with a lawyer** to prepare documents that answer these questions:

   If my parents are not able to do so,

   • *Who will handle the money?* (durable power of attorney)

   • *Who will make medical decisions?* (health care proxy)

   • *Who will assume guardianship, if needed?* (embed directive in durable power of attorney, although guardianship requires a court proceeding)

❖ Remember, a camel is a horse designed by a committee. **Sharing legal responsibility among siblings should be carefully considered.** Use impartial resources, if necessary (e.g., a lawyer for guardianship, bank trust services for finances).

❖ **Advanced directives, such as feeding tubes and DNR (Do Not Resuscitate) orders should be discussed among family members and a physician, then recorded in writing.** Paperwork for the DNR order is provided by the state.

❖ **No legal document will replace sound decision-making under stress.**

Lessons Learned: FINANCIAL

❖ **A trustworthy family member must actively supervise the finances.** Frail elders are at high risk for scams and unethical treatment. If your parents resist, give them a copy of this book, and play "what if" scenarios. Use an accountant or a bookkeeper if necessary.

❖ **Organize important papers using a simple filing system or notebook**. Include a list of all savings, investments, insurance, sources of income, and advisors (tax accountant, lawyer, investment advisor). This process may take more than one year and will be full of surprises.

❖ **Find deeds, life insurance policies, and legal documents**. Place a copy in the home filing system; file the original in a safe deposit box. You don't want to search for paperwork in a crisis.

❖ **Use software to monitor expenses and medical insurance payments**. Take time to understand insurance coverage and track reimbursement carefully.

❖ **Home health care is the least expensive option for most families**. Assisted living and nursing homes will likely consume all financial resources.

Lessons Learned: CAREGIVING

❖ **Mobility is an elder's best friend.** Keep them moving! Ask the Visiting Nurse Association or a physical/occupational therapist to adapt exercises to special needs.

❖ **Build a web of support for the ailing parent**. Draw upon family, friends, and your church or synagogue. Find resources through social workers, the local Council on Aging, the Visiting Nurse Association, and support groups such as the Alzheimer's Association.

❖ **Build a web of support for the caregiver(s)**. The emotional strain of caring for an ailing loved one often exceeds the physical strain. Find ways to reduce stress from other sources in the caregiver's life. Offer to work on house projects or assist with children; encourage vacations and daily/weekly breaks. Use respite care, if necessary. Social workers can provide ideas and resources.

❖ **Anger and guilt are a caregiver's constant companions.** Find a safe outlet for the former and a way to cope with the latter. Set limits.

❖ **Location, location!** If you don't live near your parents, consider moving them closer to you should they become frail. Investigate options, including apartments, assisted living, and continuous care communities before there is a need to do so.

❖ **Continue family traditions and celebrations.** Family relationships may be altered and strained under the pressures of elder care. Find opportunities for laughter and celebration.

Discussion Questions

1. Each child has a unique relationship with his or her parents. Explore this idea, considering the roles of the five siblings. Why were they different? Does gender matter? Education? Availability? Reflect on your own family situation.

2. Step into the shoes of Bob and Muriel. What did they do to make it easier for their children to support them as they aged?

3. Discuss the early decision Bob and Muriel made to sign a durable power of attorney. What prompted that decision? How important was that document in the events that followed? What criteria would you use to give that authority to another person? What are the risks?

4. What did you learn about navigating the medical system? How did Jan interact with medical doctors? How did she learn about treatment choices? How did she prepare for appointments? Who were her advisors?

5. How are physical ailments different from mental health ones? Talk about depression and dementia. How do these diseases affect relationships as well as treatment?

6. After Bob died, what were the choices available for Muriel's living arrangement? What choice would you have made in Jan's shoes?

7. Jan asserts that an elder's quality of life depends on the family, not the doctor. Do you agree with her? Name some specific steps she took to help her parents maintain good health and enjoy life.

8. How can you proactively help the caregiver of an elderly person? Why is that a necessary part of providing care to the elder?

9. Consider the relationship between the grandchildren and their grandparents: first, when the grandparents were healthy, and later, as they grew frail. What values or lessons were conveyed to the children by their grandparents and by their parents?

10. What motivated Jan and Ginny to support their elderly mother for four years? Is that realistic for most families?

11. What resources did Jan and Ginny use to support Muriel? How did they find support services? How did Muriel afford these services?

12. Other than terminating life support, find three incidents when Jan had to make medical choices for her parents. Discuss how those decisions were made.

13. Anger and guilt are a caregiver's constant companions. Did any incident make you angry? Why did Jan feel guilty?

14. How did Jan limit the time consumed by her mother's needs? What roles did her sister, her husband, and her children play?

15. How valuable is the experience of helping elderly parents to an adult child? What lessons did Jan learn?

Acknowledgments

A FTER WRITING A FEW CHAPTERS of this book, I met with two literary agents for guidance about book publishing. I was stunned by their interest and by their reaction to my story. One said she cried reading a segment that I intended to be amusing—she shared the sense of helplessness she felt about her now deceased mother's care. The other recounted a hilarious story about helping her father with his hygiene—he would sing his favorite tunes loudly as she washed him down. Their stories were intimate and emotive and full of vivid detail, and I was struck by their candor. We were not lifelong friends—indeed we were strangers. It was then that I glimpsed the potential impact of sharing my family's story: it gives others permission to share theirs.

I appreciate the effort of Eve Bridburg to find a home for the manuscript and the editing skill of Patrick D'Arcy, whose talent proves that youth and brilliance can coexist, even as I repeatedly have apologized to him for exposure to the end of life before he reaches the age of twenty-one. Veterans of the publishing world embraced the story with so much enthusiasm that I am indebted to them for their skill and their support. Copyeditor Betsy Dempsey took her red pen to paper with an eye for detail unsurpassed. Veteran book designer Mike Fender read the book one sleepless night, and he created a cover that captures visually the emotions I aspired to convey with words. Gayle Treadwell brought to the project her wisdom acquired over decades as a publisher and marketing guru, guiding me with great humor, while Linda Lawrence patiently directed me to embrace the marvels of social media. I am fortunate to have this dream team of experts who so joyfully support the message and the messenger.

Many friends contributed their knowledge and time reading early drafts, including Charlotte Sibley, Leif Magnusson, Esq., Piper Orton, Victoria Vitucci, Marvin Thomas, Gemma Baker, Michael Kolowich, Dr. Tom Monath, Blake Garvan, Kary Robertson, Dr. Tom Costello, Mary McGovern, Carol Kinlan, Dale Ryder, and Mary Modahl. Ginny Grant, Barbara Littlefield, Katharine Denault, and Sandy Curran were among those I could count on for help in a pinch and deserve mention for their years of friendship and support.

I remain grateful for my siblings and their genetic gifts of gab and laughter; they continue to roll with me through life's ups and downs. My admiration for my sister Ginny and her husband, Jon, has only deepened as the years have passed, and their children are a true blessing to our family. Their love is surpassed only by that from my husband, who is a rock I can stand on or be held by, as is needed, and from Eric and Katie, the joys of my life.

About the Author

JAN SIMPSON has had a distinguished career as a scientist, educator, pharmaceutical executive, and management consultant. She founded and leads *Circle of Life Partners*, a trustworthy resource for clients navigating significant life transitions, and is President of the *Benvenuti Family Foundation*. Previously, Jan led the global quality program for Bristol-Myers Squibb; served as an examiner for America's national quality award; and brought her knowledge of best practices to executives leading manufacturing, service, health care, and educational organizations. Jan has taught business practices to physicians, quality practices to business leaders, and humility to her children. She had the good fortune to be born into a large Irish family with an abundance of laughter, one that instilled the importance of family, faith, and friends. Jan holds a graduate degree in chemistry from the University of Massachusetts Lowell and an MBA from Harvard Business School.

All profits from the sale of *Don't Give Up on Me!* will be used to fund programs that serve our elders and support their caregivers or care partners.

Contact orders@colpartners.com to inquire about a volume discount for book clubs and other group purchases.